THE GRASS OF OBLIVION

By the same author: THE HOLY WELL

VALENTIN KATAYEV

The Grass of Oblivion

TRANSLATED FROM THE RUSSIAN
AND WITH AN INTRODUCTION
BY ROBERT DAGLISH

MACMILLAN · London · Melbourne · Toronto · 1969

This translation © Robert Daglish 1969
Published by
MACMILLAN AND CO LTD
Little Essex Street London WC2
and also at Bombay Calcutta and Madras
Macmillan South Africa (Publishers) Pty Ltd Johannesburg
The Macmillan Company of Australia Pty Ltd Melbourne
The Macmillan Company of Canada Ltd Toronto

The Introduction, 'Katayev and his Critics', is reprinted
from the *Anglo-Soviet Journal*, January 1968, by permission
of the Society for Cultural Relations with the U.S.S.R.

Printed in Great Britain by
NORTHUMBERLAND PRESS LIMITED
Gateshead

Katayev and his Critics

WHEN I asked Katayev if he thought his latest work had been understood in the West he made one of those characteristically Russian gestures of dismissal. 'They will talk politics all the time,' he said wrily. He was referring, I think, mainly to *The Times* reviews and the introduction to the English translation of *The Holy Well*.

It is an odd situation, and one that must genuinely puzzle some Soviet writers, when Western critics who shudder at any expression of overt political opinion in a novel or verse are observed to be hard at work digging for political allusions in the works of Soviet writers. It would be amusing to see Edward Crankshaw probing for signs of resistance to the régime in the current work of, say, Kingsley Amis and dismissing him as a 'trusty' when the search proved fruitless. But such things simply don't happen. Specialization and the cold war have bred a strain of politico-literary critic whose activities, perhaps mercifully, are confined to Soviet and East European studies.

It might be argued that the Soviet critic's approach to art is always political, but surely there is a great difference between consistent Marxist literary criticism and borrowing one's opponents' principles when it suits one and dropping them when it doesn't. But even consistent political analysis of literature has its limitations, for, as Solzhenitsyn has pointed out, it is in the nature of the creative artist to grasp by sheer intuition what can be formulated as political theory only much later. Sinyavsky has been hailed as a genius by some and convicted as a criminal by others. His writings reveal that he is neither and deserves neither literary canonization nor political imprisonment. The fact is that his importance as a writer and a thinker has been exaggerated out of all proportion by the efforts of the political hatchet-swingers on both sides of the fence. If we are ever to understand what Soviet literature is about our analysis must be more subtle and more patient.

The refreshing thing about Katayev's last two books *The Holy Well* (Harvill, 1967) and *The Grass of Oblivion* is that everyone seems to have a different opinion about them, and the favourable and unfavourable judgements come from quite unexpected quarters. Katayev has been voted the most controversial writer of the year and his latest work is to be discussed at length in the next issue of Voprosy Literatury (Problems of Literature). From what I have heard already the battle will be over such points as whether the actual writing is good or bad. Is the treatment of Bunin, Mayakovsky and others fair? Is not Katayev being too pretentious in putting himself on the same level as these great figures, in writing of their personal failings as well as their public merits? Yevtushenko is reported as having described the first of these books as a work of genius. On the pages of Yunost (the youth magazine Katayev himself founded) Vasily Aksyonov takes issue with a critic who thinks Katayev writes 'without pain'. At a friend's house I was told by one of those thoughtful, well-read engineers, of which there are so many in this country, 'It really is very distinguished prose.' A girl in a long-distance train put aside the German best-seller she had been devouring to sample my copy of The Holy Well. 'Artistically he seems to be not quite up to it,' she commented. An English student of Russian literature said, 'I shall never forgive him for what he did to Bunin.' Yet The Times thought Katayev's defence of Bunin touching. Personal reactions differ so widely it is almost as if people had been reading different books on the same subject.

This question of pretentiousness is fascinating. An English publisher who had read the chapters on Bunin said, 'I particularly liked the self-deprecating attitude Katayev himself adopts.' Yet in Russia the cry is often that Katayev in describing others makes too much of himself. Here, of course, we are up against the fact that for decades now Soviet literary memoirs have been almost completely self-effacing. If one's subject was great it just was not done to intrude one's own personality and certainly not to mention his scraggy neck, his moments of selfishness or the fact that he suffered from piles.

In any case the modern Russian's attitude to Bunin is complex. Here was a splendid writer, even a great one, better than Alexei Tolstoy, almost as good as Chekhov, certainly no mere counter-revolutionary officer or politician, and yet for some reason he had been unable to accept the revolution, had turned against it and cut himself off for ever from his own country. How had it happened? It would be a mistake to imagine that Russians, even Communist Russians, automatically attribute the fault in such cases to the other side. How had they lost him, how could a man of such integrity, such human insight have failed to understand them? And then there was the mystery of what he had written since, the books for which he had been awarded the Nobel Prize. What were they like and how could foreigners understand them? Surely that marvellous 'symphonic prose' could be fully appreciated only in Russian and by Russians? Although he is now being published again in large editions and in five- and eight-volume collections, Bunin's honest intransigence and supreme artistic skill linger like the echo of some irretrievably beautiful music in Russian minds.

And here is Katayev breaking into this dream with the equally intransigent voice of experience, of personal knowledge. And the same thing, or something similar, happens to Mayakovsky. The old, accepted images are suddenly enormously magnified, the angle of vision changes and a new, almost stereoscopic picture emerges.

To achieve this new angle Katayev has invented a new style of writing called *mauvisme*. In *The Holy Well* he describes it as follows: 'I am the founder of the latest literary school, the *mauvistes*, from the French *mauvais*—bad—the essence of which is that since everyone nowadays writes very well, you must write badly, as badly as possible, and then you will attract attention; of course, it is not so easy to learn to write badly because the competition is hellish, but the game is worth the candle and if you really learn to write rottenly, worse than anyone else, your world popularity is assured.'

Talking to a few of us who have been translating his books, Katayev refused to be tied down to any closer definition of his new approach. But in the course of the conversation he did expand it considerably. No, *mauvisme* was not just a joke. In a sense, it could even be described as a higher stage of socialist realism. For ten years, during the period of Stalin worship, Soviet aesthetics remained at a complete standstill, and even today critics and writers are hampered by patterns of thought that are essentially idealistic. They are guided by the intellect rather than the senses. They may acknowledge materialism, the primacy of matter in theory, but in practice they no longer trust the evidence of their senses. *Mauvisme* offers release from the straight-jacket of old-fashioned concepts and a return to immediacy of feeling without which art cannot live.

'After all,' Katayev went on, 'we are not just anybody, we are Soviet people.' And coming from him the phrase sounded quite unlike the standard newspaper slogan, for the next thing he said was, 'We have passed through exceptionally cruel and bloody wars and revolution, we have survived, we have ventured into outer space.' What Soviet people feel and think cannot, and should not, be forced into preconceived patterns; but they themselves must learn to trust their immediate reactions.

But this new emphasis on the primacy of matter does not drag us into a dull world of sober reality. On the contrary, we suddenly realize that we still do not know much about matter. Nor do we know what time is or how memory works. Then why should a novel follow the usual chronological rules? Why should it even be logical?

Katayev believes not only in matter as the primary and eternal source of life, but also in the emanations of matter, and speaks quite freely of the soul and of reincarnation as the artistic act of naming these emanations. All this is not at all so weird as it sounds. By introducing these imponderables into his narrative he brings us into an entirely convincing reality in which only some things are known and the rest is yet to be discovered.

He is frequently asked whether he is not merely imitating the techniques of Western writers like Joyce and Proust. *The Times* reviewer suggests that his new approach may appear sensational to his fellow countrymen but is all too familiar in the West. Katayev's answer is that these techniques began in Russian literature as far back as Gogol and Dostoevsky, long before they were tried out in the West. His contribution lies in their application to the new consciousness that has arisen in Soviet years.

Katayev does not spend all his time day-dreaming regardless of time and space amid the named and unnamed emanations of matter, scraps of recollected verse, legends, religious rites, but he is determined to give them their place; his picture would be incomplete without them. At the same time he can be incisively logical and aware of the period. On Mayakovsky's connection with the Proletarian Writers' Association, for instance:

'Most of them had no interest whatever in the living Mayakovsky as a person, as a very complex and contradictory poet, someone as independent and alone as Pushkin. For them, as he had been in the past for the Futurists, including LEF, he was a lucky find, a very useful leader, a man with tremendous driving force, behind whose broad back one could sneak without a ticket into the history of Russian literature.'

Or on Bunin:

'But the absence of any moral pressure from outside meant that Bunin ceased to choose a point of application for his abilities, his spiritual energies. He was unable to grapple with the "thousand-headed hydra of empiricism," of which Goethe had spoken, and it swallowed him up, or rather, he was blown to pieces by it, like a deep-water fish that has grown accustomed to a pressure of tens, hundreds, perhaps thousands of atmospheres and suddenly finds itself on the surface, experiencing practically no pressure at all.'

And the slices of Mayakovsky's, Bunin's, Mandelstam's, Khlebnikov's verse that he works into his pastiche are all in some not immediately obvious way driving a point home.

> I washed at night in a yard
> All frozen up with stars,
> Each ray bright and hard
> As salt upon an axe . . .
> Like salt a star melts and chars
> The icy water blacker still.
> So is death made cleaner,
> And saltier ill,
> Juster the earth—
> And more terrible.

Incidentally, all the verse quotations, like this one from Mandelstam, are written as prose, without line endings.

Katayev may not yet have founded what could really be called a new school among Soviet writers, although some notable young writers, Aksyonov and Yevtushenko, are delighted with his new approach. He certainly has advanced the art of combining biography and autobiography. In so doing he shows the essential falsity in the work of the critic who hides behind a string of political slogans or literary axioms. Katayev does not merely state his position; he portrays it. In *The Grass of Oblivion* he introduces himself quite frankly as an invented character called Rurik Pcholkin. After the revolution this Pcholkin, an ex-army officer and young poet, is sent around the villages to recruit rural correspondents for the new Soviet press. While doing so he falls into the hands of White Guards and escapes a sticky end by sheer accident. He wanders about trembling with fear, utterly lost in a snowstorm.

'He was alive, but his murdered soul lay on the iron-hard earth amid the broken maize stalks awaiting resurrection, just as another fear-blackened soul of his was lying by the gun emplacements near Smorgon, and somewhere else yet another soul that had departed agonisingly from his body on a bed in a typhus hospital to the beating of buddhist drums under the sacred lamaist writing that looked like Mendeleyev's table of elements. . . . And all this—strange to say—seemed to him wonderful, magnificent, like a work of unprecedented revolutionary art, full of divine meaning and supernatural beauty.'

So much for pretentiousness.

The Times Literary Supplement writes, 'Katayev's verdict is that Bunin was wrong to leave Russia . . . And yet Katayev must know that Bunin, had he remained, would surely have suffered the fate of others of his generation: hard labour, execution or suicide.' But is this not unjust to Katayev, or, at any rate, missing the point, for Katayev shows perfectly clearly what tremendous risks any Soviet writer who was worth his salt, and particularly Mayakovsky, encountered in the struggle to build a new literature, a new body of opinion on different principles from those of the old world? All these difficulties, all these dangers were outweighed by the joy of the few inches (call it 'great strides' if you will) of progress that have been made. And, on balance, these difficulties and dangers were infinitely preferable to the safety, the formal acknowledgement and the complete indifference that Bunin encountered in the West.

ROBERT DAGLISH

The Grass of Oblivion

. . . Or, perhaps, they were small sound detectors, intently probing the regions of space for a source of frequencies inaudible to the human ear. . . .

I believe I once said, or even wrote, that I had discovered in myself the ability to become reincarnated not only in all manner of people, but also in animals, plants, stones, household objects, and even in abstract concepts, such as subtraction, or something of the kind.

I believe everyone has this ability.

At any rate, whatever I see at the present moment instantly becomes I or I become it, quite apart from the fact that my own self, as such, is constantly changing and crowding my environment with its numberless reflections.

In all probability, since I, like everything else in the world, am crudely material, I must also be infinite, as is the matter of which I consist. Hence my constant intercommunication with all the material particles that make up the world – if, of course, the world is material, of which I am deeply convinced.

Because of our constant concern with everyday things we have long since ceased to wonder at the multiplicity of forms that make up our environment. But we have only to put worldly worries aside for a day and we at once regain the sense of belonging to the universe or, in other words, the sense of the eternal freshness and newness of existence.

Objects renovate themselves and acquire a new and higher meaning. For instance, the flower that at this moment has entered my field of vision. It was no accident that I paid such special attention to it. There is something about its shape that disturbs me.

Mushrooms sprouting from old tree stumps, for instance, grow in the same kind of clusters. A nest of long tubes emerging from a single node. Little sausages. Frost-bitten fingers. A bunch of young blunt-nosed carrots. As the flowers grow they change their colour, from saffron orange, to red. Their tips burst and fan out. But these are not the usual trumpet creepers that everyone knows, not at all. They are like long, narrow bells, and their softly rounded mouths, festooned with petals, radiate a tigerish apricot colour, ominously inflamed at the heart of the flower, into which insects crawl, as though hypnotized, to their execution.

A Buddhist red colour.

These flowers grow quickly and just as quickly fade, wilt, wither and drop out of the ripe pedicel, leaving behind them a long semi-transparent axis with the taut green dew-drop of the ovary at its tip.

And so, instead of working, I sit observing the flowers and

rejoicing that they remind me of many other objects, including those semi-transparent rubber nipples that are put on bottles of baby's milk, and then I go off in search of the gardener to find out the name of this flower. All my emotions are concentrated on this idle question. Does it really matter what it is called, this in some way agonizingly familiar plant, whose strong stems climb the posts of the veranda and continually, almost deliberately, push into my face the saffron-red blossoms, recalling something I once cherished? And now I have noticed something else. In this cluster there are blossoms of all ages, from the very smallest, the little half-grown acorns, the midgets, the dwarfs no bigger than a thumbnail, to crimson velvet beauties in full bloom, king blossoms, and finally to blossoms that are now corpses, their empty colourless sheaths exhibiting the terrifying spectacle of brown decay. And all of them – the whole cluster, the whole family, the living and the dead – lie strictly parallel to the balustrade of the veranda, all pointing in one direction – towards the eternally setting sun that is already touching the mountainous horizon.

The gardener said that this flower was called a 'bignonia.' Well, so much the better.

A long horizontal stem with pinnate opposite leaves, branching out of the hot, dusty bush, offered me a flower cluster and the largest blossom of all, like Pieretta's fancy-dress cap, stopped before my eyes, and then I quite easily and without any effort recalled just such another sultry June morning, the Kovalevsky Tower in Odessa and an open veranda with Pompeian plaster vases, which at the time I took to be marble, while the house itself seemed at least an ancient Roman villa after the style of the painter Semiradsky and even the modest strip of not very beautiful Black Sea, with the harsh cries of bathers coming from it, appeared to my eyes as the glittering Bay of Naples dotted with red sails. And all this occurred because I was about to see a man whose talent I worshipped and who was almost a legend to me.

'Someone to see you, Vanya!' a small plump man called out in a clipped Moscow accent.

We guessed at once that this was Ivan Alexeyevich's elder brother, also a man of letters, who wrote on educational subjects.

'Who is it?' came the reply from within.

'Some young poets.'

'Just a minute.'

And on the threshold of the veranda, buttoning on his foreign braces, there appeared Academician Bunin himself. He gave us a quick glance and at once disappeared, but a minute later re-emerged in quite a different rhythm and fully dressed.

Many people have described Bunin's appearance. I think the most successful was Andrei Bely: the profile of a condor, tear-washed eyes, and so on. I have forgotten the rest.

Later I heard that Bunin's eyes were a wonderful light-blue, but I never noticed it. Maybe they were.

Before us stood a gentleman of forty – dry, bilious, dapper – over whom shone the halo of Honoured Academician, division of *belles-lettres*. Later I realized that he was not so much bilious as haemorrhoidal, but that is of no importance.

Well cut trousers. English tan-leather shoes with thick soles. The everlasting kind. A dark-brown goatee, a writer's goatee, but more carefully tended and more pointed than Chekhov's. A French one. Not for nothing had Chekhov called him in jest Monsieur Bouquichon. A pince-nez like Chekhov's, steel-rimmed, but not on his nose – folded in two and tucked into the side pocket of his casual sporting jacket, which may have had a very fine check.

A starched collar, high and firm, the points swept well back over the conventional violet necktie, like the corners of two visiting cards made of the very best Bristol board. In the twenties I should most certainly have described it as a Bristol collar. In those days we used to call that transference of epithet, a literary device I believe I invented – and terribly abused. A kind of inversion. So there you are.

But in those days the twenties were a long way off, a whole eternity!

I hesitate to write like that now, for I am growing old and staid. It is time to think about the soul. Now I have become a *mauvist*.

Bunin eyed us with stern formality and from a great distance held out his hands to us – one to me, the other to Vovka Dietrichstein – not to shake hands, but to receive our poems.

Vovka Diederiks, or, as he was in the habit of signing his work, Vl. von Dietrichstein, was also a young poet, but much older than I. A rich student wearing not the usual uniform but cream flannel trousers, a short garish jacket, a firm straw boater, a thick gold signet ring with the family seal on it, and whose face was the blond monkey-like face of a Baltic German with prominent widely spaced teeth. A typical last surviving heir.

Obeying Bunin's immobile stare, we placed our compositions in his outstretched hands. Vovka's contribution was a book of decadent verse, which he had just had printed at his own expense on watermarked cream-laid paper with a two-colour binding that bore the title *The Faded Wreath*. Mine was a general exercise book, which I pulled out from under my school belt with its battered metal buckle.

Gripping our compositions firmly in his strong fingers, Bunin told us to come back in a fortnight, bowed politely with a mere nod of the head, indicating that the audience was over, and withdrew, and his brother Yuli said that Vanya had to go to a party and accompanied us for a few paces along the stone veranda to the steps, which led down to the garden path covered with dusty, grinding gravel, like all the paths in the suburbs of Odessa.

9

Exactly two weeks later – to the minute – we were again standing on the stone flags of that familiar veranda, over the rail of which trailed the crimson-orange sausage-like blossoms of the flower whose name I did not yet know and was to discover only fifty years later.

'Vanya, someone to see you,' said the small plump man, addressing the door.

'Who?' came an irritable voice from inside.

'The young poets.'

'Just a minute.'

And once more Bunin appeared at the glass door, with our compositions in his outstretched hands and, making no mistake, handed Vovka his graceful volume, and me, my exercise book.

'I have read your verses,' he said sternly, like a doctor, addressing his remarks mainly to Vovka. This irritated me, for it once more confirmed my observation that, however small the company I happened to be in, I was either not noticed at all, or was the last to be noticed; it was a feature of my character. 'Well, what shall I say? It's hard to say anything positive. Personally, I don't accept this kind of poetry.'

Vovka smiled foolishly but arrogantly.

'You,' Bunin went on, 'ought to go and see one of the decadents – Balmont, for example. As for me, I find it difficult to say. Mannered. Coy. Indefinite, vague, pretentious. And quite often, simply not Russian—'

'Yes, but don't you acknowledge the nonsensical in poetry?' Vovka interrupted him boldly, licking his wet, shapeless little lips. 'Many people do today.'

'Possibly. But I presume that if something is nonsensical, it has no sense in it, in other words, that it is absurd,' Bunin said.

I trembled to think that a real literary aphorism had actually come to life in my presence, but I kept my head and at once offered Bunin a large brown photograph of himself mounted in grey passe-partout, which I had bought the day before for one rouble in silver from a photographer who had been keeping it for advertisement in the window of his studio in Richelieu Street, in the famous Odessa five-storey sky-scraper built in Moorish style out of yellow brick.

The photograph – concealed under a flap of tissue-paper, like a bride under her bridal veil – showed Bunin sitting rather sideways in an iron garden chair, his bony hands gripping its arms, and with one leg hooked over the other and both of them sticking out so that his foreign shoes were right in the foreground and looked unnaturally large, with every detail, the thick soles, the holes punched round the seams, the leather laces tied in a bow, clearly visible while the Academician's impressive head with its aristocratic bulge at the back appeared far less impressive than I should have liked; even the high-grade garden gravel in the foreground had come out far more expressively than any of the other accessories.

When I had seen his photograph in the window I had run home and almost with tears in my eyes extorted from my aunt the rouble that the incompetent but astute photo-grapher had asked when he saw he was confronted by a young poet-admirer of a metropolitan celebrity.

I now produced this photograph from a yellowed piece of newspaper and presented it to Bunin.

'Do you want me to autograph this?' Bunin asked in-differently, but, strange though it may seem, I suddenly realized that somewhere at the back of his mind he was flattered both by my confusion and his photograph, to which he gave only a glance, instantly perceiving all its provincia-lity, from the grey passe-partout mounting to the third-rate tissue-paper. 'But what shall I write – that is the question.'

'If you can, I mean, if you don't mind, write what you said just now.'

Bunin looked surprised. 'What did I say?'

'Well . . . You said what is nonsensical is absurd.'

'Did I say that?'

'Of course you did.'

Bunin thought for a minute, then took a fountain-pen out of the inside pocket of his jacket – in those days a fountain-pen was a great novelty – and unscrewed the top.

'Very well. What is your name?'

I told him.

He placed the photograph on the plaster balustrade and in clear cuneiform characters wrote across the top left-hand corner, where the accessories were not so dense, 'To Valentin Katayev. What is nonsensical is absurd. Iv. Bunin.'

I was beside myself with joy, and Vovka Dietrichstein bit his wet lips with envy, cursing himself for not having thought of buying a photograph of Bunin.

The thing I liked best was the big capital Cyrillic Б in Bunin's signature, particularly the top stroke, which was at first exceptionally thick and then gradually tapered like an Assyrian cuneiform character, or a fat horizontal exclamation mark, or perhaps a horse-radish with a very thin tail. I say nothing of how flattering it was to see my own name inscribed in the hand of the famous writer.

This time Bunin saw us off as far as the veranda steps and shook hands, first with Vovka, then with me.

And then a miracle happened. The first miracle in my life.

As Vovka Dietrichstein turned away down the steps Bunin held me back gently by the sleeve of my rough school tunic and murmured quietly, as though to himself:

'Come over one morning and we'll have a chat.'

As he spoke, he carefully pulled the exercise book from under my arm and concealed it behind his back.

My state of mind during the four or five days that for the sake of politeness I forced myself with the greatest difficulty to wait, instead of running off to see Bunin on the very next day, can easily be imagined.

But at last I was flying along in an empty morning tram with folding wickerwork seats, heading for the Kovalevsky

Villa. On the left the sea kept appearing and disappearing amid the dusty greenery beyond the cliffs, and on the right there were glimpses of suburban squares strewn with the dry husks of sunflower seed, dotted with lemonade stalls, bakers' stalls and post-offices, and even in one place an open-air theatre with a plaster lyre over the entrance, where amateur shows were held, and the tram's collector-arm swished along the copper cable, scattering sparks that in the brilliance of the dazzling morning sun and the equally dazzling sea seemed black as coal, and the cable sang like a 'cello and at the sharp bends the brakes screeched and moaned, and I stood on the platform of the brand new Belgian car, holding on to an iron post, and hung out of the open door to let the wind cool my burning close-cropped head.

Then stillness, the deserted garden of the villa, the crunch of the dusty gravel, the wormwood-scented wind from the steppes, the stone veranda and the red blossoms of the as yet unnamed though already familiar flower. At the entrance to one of the blossoms, which in the sunshine glowed red as a cock's comb, a wasp was hovering.

One day, long afterwards, I was to read in Pasternak those magical lines: '. . . voices approaching: Scriabin. Oh, where shall I flee from the footsteps of my idol!'

The worn flag-stones of the veranda resounded under those same foreign shoes. He was wearing a freshly ironed blouse of unbleached linen, the breast pocket saddled with a pince-nez on a black cord.

But something must have changed in the world, or was about to change – something fateful and irreparable – because, although the morning was as hot and sunny as ever, the villa no longer seemed to me a Roman villa and over the rectangle of ruffled Black Sea I could see no red sails of the Bay of Naples, and the room to which my host invited me was as simple as a caretaker's, with white walls and a brightly painted floor, in the ambre-ochre boards of which hung the sky-blue reflection of a small window, and with a kitchen table neatly covered with a sheet of red blotting-paper firmly fixed down with drawing pins, on which I noticed a folded sheet of notepaper with a few lines written on it, and on the hot glowing window-sill, on another folded sheet of the same notepaper a heap of damp Turkish tobacco drying in the sun and, beside it, a box of aethereally white cigarette tubes from the Konelsky Factory, a steel gadget for packing them, its copper clasps gleaming in the sun, and a steel rod with a plain round wooden handle, all prepared for making a fresh cigarette, while the air was still wreathed with the faint blue fumes of the one that had just been smoked, and Bunin himself no longer seemed to me so severe and there was something more Chekhovian in his beard than there had been on my last visit. We sat down on two bent-wood chairs, as light and resonant as musical instruments, and he placed on the table my oilcloth-covered exercise book, smoothed it with his dry palm and said:

'Now then!'

. . . but how had all this happened? What did we have in common? Why was I so passionately fond of him? Only a short time ago I had never even heard of the man. I knew Kuprin, Andreyev, Gorky, I had heard of Artsybashev, Yushkevich, Chirikov – yes, the one of whom that sharp old man Leo Tolstoy was said to have remarked, 'What's his name – Tsurikov, Churikov . . .' – but of Bunin I knew absolutely nothing. And all of a sudden, one fine day he became my idol.

Let us look into the matter.

I had been writing verse for some time and, like all young poets, was in a state of constant mental upheaval. I did the round of the local newspaper offices without any attempt at selection, I read my poems to anyone I happened to come across at school, during the intervals between lessons. I would ask the opinion of my friends, my family, my father, my aunt. I tortured my younger brother Zhenya – the Evgeni

Petrov of later years – with my works. I sent my poems to my grandmother in Ekaterinoslav, I even acquired a reputation for being slightly mad among the girls I knew at school. And this was all because no one could explain to me what I then thought must be the great secret, no one could reveal to me the cherished mystery of poetry which, unless I discovered it, might easily make me really mad because I could not understand why all this was being written, what was the significance of all these rhymes, measures and stanzas that had been known ever since the days of Lomonosov, that had been written a thousand times before, and read and re-read a thousand times and had, in fact, as far as essential meaning went, nothing whatever to do with me, my life, my future, my interests, all these insipid 'Cold is the breath of Nature mute, wildly the grey waves foam and seethe,' and so on and so forth.

. . . Asterisks between verses. . . .

Mayakovsky, about whom I shall also have something to say in this book, must have experienced the same feeling in his time. In his biography he writes:

'It came out stilted and excruciatingly tearful. Something like this: "In gold and purple the forests were clad. On roofs and domes the sun was shining, I waited, but the days all lapsed into months, hundreds of days of weary repining."

'I filled a whole notebook with it. . . .'

No one could tell me anything, and I heard nothing but, 'Just imagine, Valya writes poetry. But then, everyone writes poetry at his age.'

At the editorial offices:

'Poetry? Splendid. Leave it with us and come back in a fortnight. No manuscripts returned.'

A fortnight later:

'No good.'

'Why not?'

'Because we're literally snowed under with poetry and we don't really publish it.'

Or, a sudden stroke of luck:

'We've taken one.'

'Which?'

'Oh, I don't remember now. Something about nature. Eight lines. As a filler.'

And only once, in the offices of the *Odessa News*, surrounded by narrow thumb-marked proof-sheets, the famous journalist Gertso-Vinogradsky, who over the pseudonym of Lohengrin ran a daily satirical column of short, chopped up lines and one-syllable paragraphs in the style of that king of newspaper satirists the great Vlas Doroshevich, a man with a thin, intellectual face and long Verhaeren moustache, shot a glance at me through the Chekhovian steel-rimmed pince-nez that everyone seemed to wear in those days, for apparently something about me – it would be hard to say what – had interested him. Or perhaps it was just ordinary human sympathy, because I was coughing so unnaturally in embarrassed imitation of 'weak lungs,' and was so nervously crushing the patent-leather peak of my school cap, which had been burned through in several places with a magnifying glass, and was so ashamed of the volcanic rash of growth pimples on my thin Chinese chin. Anyway, he gently pushed aside my roll of poems with a kindly hand and spoke with a simple frankness that staggered me.

'Now, listen. Suppose I ask you to come back in a week, and then tell you your poetry won't do because we don't publish poetry anyway, even though we do occasionally, or because the poems are half-baked, although they may well be only half-baked. What will it all add up to? Do you want to know the gospel truth? You have brought me some poems and I – I give you my word as a man of honour – know absolutely nothing about poetry and can, therefore, give you no worthwhile advice. And no one on this newspaper knows a damned thing about poetry. You can take my word for it. They only pretend they do. So my advice to you – take your poems to a real writer and let him read them. A *real* writer – understand?'

He stressed the word and stared at me with kindly sclerotic eyes.

'Living here in Odessa,' he said, 'we have one real writer – I don't count Yushkevich. And he is Alexander Mitrofanovich Fyodorov. You've probably heard of him?'

'No, never.'

'Chekhov liked his poem: "Outside the window a barrel-organ plays. My window's open, dusk is falling".' He took off his pince-nez and wiped away real tears with a handkerchief. 'There, you see. And you want to be a writer! You ought to know him! A. Fyodorov. His name's in the encyclopaedia!'

I felt terribly ashamed of my ignorance and maintained a guilty silence, crushing my cap in my lowered hands and breaking metal twigs out of the badge. But then I had an inspiration. A. M. Fyodorov!

Was this not the father of that polytechnic student, Vitka Fyodorov, I had been rather friendly with when we lived together in Otrada? I remembered Vitka boasting that his father was a writer.

'He doesn't live in Otrada, does he?'

'He used to. Now he has built his own summer place near the Kovalevsky Tower.'

'I'm a friend of his son Vitka.'

'That's right. He has a son called Vitka. Well, I advise you seriously then – don't put it off, go and see him. He's a good poet, a pupil of Maikov,' he added in a mysterious whisper. 'He can give you some useful advice. It's the only sensible thing you can do. What's the matter – something wrong with your lungs?'

'No, they're all right. I was just coughing. It's very hot in your office.'

'God bless you.'

Since there was not a soul in the house, I walked freely through all the rooms and halted at the half-open door of a study where I saw someone who, as I realized at once, must

17

be A. M. Fyodorov himself, seated at a desk against the back-drop of a huge Venetian window with expensive brass bolts that stretched right across one wall, about a third of it being taken up by the sea, the Bolshoi Fontan shore and the light-house, while two thirds were filled with the huge moving overcast sky of early spring, still cold and bleak from storms, and with unbelievably large horse-chestnut buds which looked as though they had been thickly smeared with joiner's glue.

A. M. Fyodorov was thoughtfully, between pauses, mak-ing entries in a massive notebook. He must be writing poetry, I thought, and walked into the room, horribly conscious of the squeaking of my new shoes.

'Good morning,' I said, and coughed.

He gave a tremendous start and threw back his small hand-some head with its finely chiselled, slightly hooked nose and very small silvery beard. A real European writer, good-looking, a person from some quite different, much higher world; such people were quite beyond my ken. I saw at once that he was refined and yet exquisitely natural, an intellec-tual to the very finger-tips, as was demonstrated by the casual batiste necktie, the velvet working jacket, and the amber cigarette-holder, which imparted to his presence some-thing in the very highest degree artistic.

'Good morning,' I said again, bowing and scraping my foot.

He pressed the tips of his fingers to his greying temples. A gleam of frenzy appeared in his eyes.

'What a ghastly shock you gave me! You must not do things like that. I thought, God knows – a fire or something. What do you want?'

'I'm a friend of Vitka's.'

'Vitka is at school,' he said in some perplexity. 'Why aren't you? Or has something happened to Vitka?' he shouted, jumping to his feet. 'For Heaven's sake, tell me what!'

'Nothing.'

'Is he alive?'

'Yes, I expect so. Why?'

'Why?! That's what I should be asking you. Why aren't you at school?'

I shrugged.

'This is very odd.'

'I didn't come to see Vitka. I've come to see you.'

'To see me?' Fyodorov repeated in surprise.

But before I could pull my manuscripts out of the pocket of my greatcoat, he realized what it was all about and began to writhe like a wounded animal.

'Poetry? No, not now, I implore you! Can't you see I'm busy? I never receive anyone at his hour. How did you get in here?'

He recoiled from me and stared in horror at my manuscripts that I was already fumbling with. We were alone in the house. He was trapped.

'Lyda!' he cried in a feeble voice, but his wife had gone to town shopping, and he gave in with a gesture of despair.

Bathed in sweat and coughing all the time, I read him my poems. In the languid, well modulated voice of a famous writer, much spoiled by women, he made a few casual remarks, then got into his stride and, when I laid aside my manuscript, he looked at me with a rather humorous gleam in his eye, stroking the small tassel of his silvery beard. 'Very well, then,' he said with mellifluous sweetness. 'Now it's my turn. Hold tight, Valya, I'm going to slay you.' And with these words he drew a thick morocco-leather notebook out of his desk and with relish began to reel off the sonnets which, so he explained, he had composed all at one sitting the night before during a fit of insomnia: ' "Grey sideburns. A piercing eye. So Shylock stands and with uneven teeth and hasty hands the cherished bundle he unties wherein a wondrous treasure lies – a pearl from Persian waters raised, from dark to light. And jealously he gazed. . . ." ' And so on, and then the gorgeous ending: ' ". . . it lives and breathes, but, God, I hear a sigh: Why, diver, didst thou take me from the deep to feast this avaricious eye?" '

Naturally, I was slain at a stroke. Here was a real poet! And from that day on I became a devoted admirer and pupil of Fyodorov, who soon grew used to me and not without a certain languid satisfaction would say to his friends, 'This is Valya. A young poet. My gifted pupil. We read our poems to each other.'

This idyllic life went on for quite a long time, but was cut short rather suddenly, when one day Fyodorov, carried away by his feelings, said languidly, 'Ach, Valya. . . . It's all nonsense, you know, really. My teacher Maikov considered me a talented pupil and predicted a brilliant future for me,' his gaze wandered to an autographed photograph of the poet, an old man with a silvery black beard, wearing stern metal-rimmed spectacles, 'but, to be quite frank, are we really poets? Bunin now – there's a real poet. Have you read Bunin?'

'No.'

'You don't know Bunin's poetry?' Fyodorov exclaimed in horror. 'And have never heard anything about him?'

'Vaguely,' I lied. 'In some magazine. Rather long and tedious. No rhyme even. But perhaps it wasn't Bunin.'

Fyodorov looked at me with silent reproach, went over to the huge bookcase that stretched right across one wall, took a book off one of the shelves and began to page through it.

I caught a glimpse of an inscription with a large cuneiform capital letter Б.

' "The sea is a pearly mirror," ' Fyodorov read out, holding the open book in his hand but not looking into it; he read in a fine, rather affected tenor and his voice trembled with genuine admiration. ' "The lilac is milky gold. How warm it has grown before sunset, how fragrant the smoke over hut and fold. Now a seagull in a rocky inlet has settled. . . ." ' At this point Fyodorov turned his small, well-proportioned head and looked out of the window over the wide expanse of the Black Sea, narrowing his eyes slightly, as though he could actually see the Caucasian coast with its highlander's hut, the rocky inlet and the seagull that had settled there. . . . ' "Now a seagull in a rocky inlet has settled, like a fisherman's float it moors . . . and silver streams from its pink legs as it soars." '

I was thunderstruck. A very simple secret of poetry that had so stubbornly eluded me until now, driving me almost to despair, was now revealed to me.

I had long been aware – though perhaps vaguely – that one did not become a poet just by making up verses. The ease of versification no longer deceived me. Although the outward appearance of poetry, so different from prose, with its couplets and quatrains, the elegant way the page was set up in print, the triple asterisks, the dotted lines, and all the other well-known tricks, still exerted a hypnotic influence over me, I was beginning at times to find them irritating. I had even conceived the idiotic idea that one could write down all the existing pairs of rhymes in a little notebook, learn off by heart, like a multiplication table, all the existing poetic metres – iambics, choreas, amphibrachs – it would not take a great deal of effort – and the trick was done! As for the subjects, they were generally known and readily available: dreams, longings, sorrow, yearning, love, gardens, the moon, rivers, lovers' meetings, passion, flowers, autumn, spring, winter, summer (less often), kisses, night, morning, evening, noon (less often), betrayal, a bitter fate. . . . And, of course, there was plenty of sea, waves, storms, bays, seagulls, and so on. But it was all *general*. Bays were certainly one of the ingredients. But they were bays in general. Something bookish rather than real. Something that evoked no clear image in the mind.

But here we had not just a bay but an inlet and, secondly, not any kind of inlet but a rocky inlet, just like many that I had seen and admired along the Arkadia or Maly

Fontan coast without ever suspecting that it was a fitting subject for poetry. The seagull, too, was not an abstract sea-gull of vignettes and tail-pieces, but a real Black Sea seagull – friend of the Bolshoi Fontan Beacon – which in this case had settled in a rocky inlet like a fisherman's float, a comparison whose simplicity and yet almost scientific accuracy literally took my breath away. If anyone did, I certainly knew how those half-red and half-blue cork floats lightly rode the incoming waves with goose-feathers sticking out of their tops.

Bunin opened my eyes to the physical fact of the fisherman's float, which – visibly – had the same specific gravity as a seagull with its hollow bones and close-knit but extremely light, oily, waterproof feathering saturated, as it were, with air.

The silver water streaming off those pink and also waterproof legs was as authentic – nowadays I would call it stereoscopic – as if I had seen it in a good pair of naval binoculars that could magnify things about fifteen times.

I saw the miracle of true poetry; a new world was revealed to me. That very evening I asked my father to buy me a book of Bunin's verse. My father looked at me through his pince-nez with eyes that, I believe, were filled with tears of joy. His young bumpkin of a son had come to his senses at last. This time he wanted not skates, not a football, not an air pistol, not a tennis racket, but a book. And not Conan Doyle's *Sherlock Holmes* or Gaston Leroux's *Yellow Room Mystery*, but the wonderful work of a Russian poet. Perhaps it was the only truly happy day in his whole life. Fathers will understand this. And so will children – not now, but in the course of time.

The next day, as soon as he came home from school, father presented me with a volume wrapped in excellent thin, strong brown paper that smelt of the Educational Stationer's gaslight and globes, maps and lithographs. It was a plump volume of Ivan Bunin's poetry published by Znaniye in 1906 in a dull greenish grained paper cover that had something elusively Social-Democratic about it.

And now I was sitting in front of the living Ivan Bunin, watching his hand as it slowly turned the pages of my exercise-book. Those dog-eared pages were edged in red and at the corners there were little drawings of a human figure in various poses, so that if you flipped the pages fanwise they created a miniature moving picture of a little fellow waving his arms and legs, as in the animated cartoons of today. The action could last several seconds, depending on the thickness of the exercise-book.

On the corners of the thickest of all the gymnasium textbooks, *Nature Study*, certain assiduous students had managed to illustrate a boxing-match or the fatal pole jump into the water performed by that legendary circus artist Dazzarila.

Ignoring the little men on the corners, Bunin turned the pages of my exercise-book, its black oil-cloth cover scored with anchors, hearts and arrows. He paused over some of the poems, reading them over to himself several times, then made a few brief remarks about some point of accuracy or grammar, but they were all brief, business-like and quite inoffensive. When he could not understand my handwriting he would put on his pince-nez and ask, 'What word is that?'

And it was quite impossible to tell whether he liked the poems or not.

Many years later I was to hear Stanislavsky speaking to one of the actors at a rehearsal of *The Embezzlers*:

'You may act well or you may act badly, just as you like. I don't care. All that matters to me is that you should act *the truth*.'

I believe Bunin was looking for some little flash of truth in my poems. Nothing else mattered.

When he reached one poem in which I described autumn at a villa (it was A. M. Fyodorov's villa, of course), Bunin read it through in a quiet, leisurely way and stopped at the last verse, in which I expressed in poetic form the thought that the poet was also a painter (A. M. Fyodorov was indeed also a painter) and by painting a still-life of some asters in a jug had, as it were, saved these late flowers from death and on his canvas given them eternal life, or something of that kind.

'A vase of blossoms that in autumn flower, saved by the poet from early blight, last survivors of beauty's bower, living in dreams of lost delight.'

Bunin winced as though from toothache.

'What were you actually trying to say here?' he asked. 'It sounds like Fyodorov's studio upstairs at his villa, where he paints his still-lifes. Is that it? In that case it would have been better to put it like this.'

Bunin crossed out the last verse with his pencil and wrote in the margin:

'Autumn flowers upon the table, saved by the poet from early death.'

He thought for a moment, then ended firmly: 'Sketch-boxes. Crumpled canvases. And someone's hat upon the easel.'

I was astonished at the accuracy, the brevity, the substantiality with which Bunin's three strokes of the brush amid my vague, general lines had suddenly brought to life his friend Fyodorov's studio by selecting its essential details – the sketch-boxes, the crumpled canvases, the soft-brimmed hat, and the easel.

Such economy of words!

With amazing clarity I saw the heavy, roughly built, paint-splashed easel and hanging from it the velvet hat, its brim artistically bent in Tyrolean style, which so perfectly conveyed Fyodorov's character with his elegant dilettantism and his innocent attempts to appear Bohemian.

For some reason I often found myself imagining afterwards that just such a velvet olive-coloured hat with its brim bent up one side and down the other in Tyrolean style was worn by one of the famous critics of the day Yuli Eichenwald. And, perhaps, by Kornei Chukovsky as well.

I must confess I was slightly put off by the 'crumpled canvases.' Artists' canvases are rarely crumpled. They are either stretched over a frame or stand rolled up in a corner. Try to crumple them! To this day I am troubled by those crumpled canvases, which show that even the best poets sometimes make use of trite epithets, which may appear accurate but are essentially false, left in the hope that they will pass unnoticed.

But I noticed this one because I had never seen any crumpled canvases, although I had seen them rolled up, heavy with paint. But this is all by the way.

Bunin paused for a moment over another of my poems in which I described a meeting with a high-school girl at sunset in autumn in a country churchyard. This was all quite true to life and had actually happened quite recently in the village of Usatovy Khutora, near Odessa, where I had been staying with a friend.

I watched Bunin's eyes scanning my lines: 'We came and, musing, sat alone together on a grave, while dreamily a choir of crickets chanted crystal clear, and in the wind the sere everlastings waved 'mid tomb and cross of stone' – and so on. 'And suddenly I felt sad, and lonely, but only for a moment, for you were with me, and in the deep blue sky the icy sickle of the moon stood high.'

Bunin paused for a while over this poem, as though to share my experience of sitting on the cold limestone tomb in a country churchyard by the light of an icy moon that silvered the mica-like everlastings around us, and then with my chewed stump of pencil put a tick at the top of the page which seemed to indicate that the poem was not too bad, at any rate 'true.'

Only two poems in the whole book were marked with ticks and I felt despondent at the thought that I had failed in the eyes of Bunin and would never make a good poet, particularly since he had nothing encouraging to say to me in parting. Just the usual remarks of one who was quite indifferent: 'Not bad. Go on writing. Observe nature. Poetry means working every day.'

He did develop the idea of working every day at some length.

'One must write poetry every day, just as a violinist or a pianist must play every day on his instrument for several hours without fail. If not, your talent will stagnate and run dry, like a well from which no water is drawn. What should you write about? Anything you choose. If you have no special subject, no idea, simply write about everything you see. You see a dog running along with its tongue lolling,' he said, glancing out of the window. 'Describe that dog. One or two verses. But with real accuracy, true to life, so it is that dog and no other. Describe a tree. The sea. A bench. Find the only true definition for them. Describe the sound of gravel under a girl's sandals as she runs down to the sea with a towel over her shoulder and her water wings in her hand. What kind of sound is it? It's not a squeak, not a ringing sound. Not a rustle. And yet it is all of them and something else besides – something *gravelly*, demanding the only essential and right word. Or describe, for instance, this creeping bush of red flowers that are climbing up over the balustrade, and want to look in the window, through the glass doors to see what you and I are doing here. It's a very typical plant for a Bolshoi Fontan villa, for the month of June, for a sultry noon, when there is no one in the garden because everyone has gone to bathe and the clamour and cries of the girls as they enter the water can be heard coming from the shore.'

I became entirely absorbed in examining the ripe red flower, already touched with the first signs of decay. Little yellowed teeth barred the wasp's path into the dark-red heart of the dying blossom, where there glowed grim fires of war and revolution whose approach was as yet outside my consciousness. Another blossom was dead, and the tiny red ants filing up a plaster pillar of the balustrade were already swarming over its dead flesh.

Once again I see those small, fragile ants and they seem to me to be the very same ones. Perhaps they are the same ones – these fragile, short-lived ants, eternal and mindless in their instinctive search through the huge unknowable world for the body of a decaying flower. But what is its name? Now I know. But then I did not.

I have noticed that men are usually three times more troubled by the appearance of a thing if they have no name for it. The ability to name the things around us is perhaps the only feature that distinguishes man from other beings. But I lack the words to name millions of creatures, concepts and things that surround me. This troubles me. But the thing that has no name endures even worse torment: its life is not complete. Crowds of unnamed objects suffer torment around me and in their turn torment me with the terrible realization that I am not a god. Things and concepts without names stand in the glass cabinets of eternity like the freshly gilded figures of as yet non-incarnate Buddhas in the dark confines of a temple in a burning stone-flagged courtyard under the faded sky of Mongolia, which seems to breathe the sacrificial smoke of scorched desert plants, the drowsy aroma of the yellow poppy, of sage, wormwood and the thousand-year-old tiles of the Chinese roof of the belled palace of Bogdo Gegen.

The Buddhas are all alike and have no individuality. The gold leaf is fresh and their long smiles express no ideas; they await their incarnation but this can happen only when some entirely new concept demanding plastic expression appears in the world.

Then the shaven-headed lamas, like Roman senators in red tunics and canary-yellow togas – though not in sandals but in Mongolian boots – take from one of those glass cabinets a nameless Buddha, give it a name and carry him to the

27

temple, where amid the smoke of smouldering torches, fervent cries, whirling prayer drums, beautiful chocolate sweets and crêpe-de-Chine ritual kerchiefs he at last becomes a god.

. . . The red Buddhist colour, the golden jazz of sacrifices.

'And, if it comes to that, you can describe a sparrow,' said Bunin. 'I know you are in despair because everything has been said already, there are no new subjects or new feelings, all the rhymes have been used up long ago and are worn to tatters: the possible metres can be counted on the fingers of one hand, and what it all boils down to is that to become a poet is quite impossible. As a young man I had similar thoughts that drove me to the point of insanity. But they are all nonsense, my dear sir. Every object within your ken, every feeling you possess is a theme for a poem. Listen to your feelings, observe what is going on in the world around you, and write. But write what you feel, and what you see, and not what other poets, even the most brilliant, have felt and seen before you. In art you must be independent. That is something that can be learned. And then an inexhaustible world of poetry will be revealed to you. And you will find it easier to breathe.'

But already I was breathing easily and looking at all that surrounded me with new, eager eyes.

. . . Having carefully described a sparrow, I began to describe a girl. But she was neither a bird nor a flower. It was not enough to say that she was thirteen, that she wore a short skirt, evidently made out of cast-offs, had thin legs tanned almost black and encrusted to the knees with the pearly grains of wet sea sand, a sailor's blouse with a bleached blue collar that revealed her sharp collar bones and a close-cropped, blue-black, curly, I should say Grecian, head that at first sight one wanted to compare with a blackberry.

She looked up at me as she passed the plaster vases of the

28

balustrade and I saw a thin, olive-dark face with narrow eyes full of mysterious moonlight.

Her lips, blue from bathing, curled scornfully and with a shrug of her shoulders she darted out of sight, humiliated by her obvious poverty and yet fierce and proudly independent, like a little hungry princess.

By now she was much more than a brilliant discovered detail of the midday summer beach, an excuse for word painting, a lesson in poetry.

I was suddenly completely aware of her not as a mere girl but as the tragic heroine of a future novel, not something contrived but something real and about to take shape. . . .

. . . Miracle of a landscape changing instantly into an epic, a tragedy.

I knew that we should meet again some time.

A few days later I was pestering my friends with the story of how I had met Bunin; on hardly anyone did it make the slightest impression. I must repeat that my Bunin was little known. Only those of my friends among the young poets to whose circle I by that time officially belonged took any interest in my story. True, the majority of them refused to acknowledge Bunin as a poet, a fact which drove me to despair and a kind of childish frenzy. But they were all overawed by the fact that he was a member of the Academy and, on learning that Bunin, who was known for his strict judgement, had placed a tick of approval against two out of fifteen of my poems, at first refused to believe it, but having seen with their own eyes Bunin's own version about the hat on the easel, acquired a certain interest in me, although they were still inclined to shrug their shoulders. They did not acknowledge me as a poet either. In those days no one recognized anyone at all. It was a sign of good literary taste.

Just as it is today, incidentally.

I had become something of a celebrity and my exercisebook with Bunin's lines in it was soon so badly thumbed that I had to show it to people from a distance, without allowing it to be touched.

The fame went to my head. I rejoiced in this new happiness, in the promise of fresh wonders to come. Tirelessly I made up poems one after another, describing everything around me. I realized that poetry was not at all what it was commonly supposed to be. Much more often it lay in what was not considered to be poetry at all. There was no need to seek it, to dig it up from somewhere. It was there, right at hand – one had only to be inwardly aware of its presence. And this inward awareness of life as poetry now took complete possession of me.

And this was because I had suddenly discovered, understood with all my soul, that poetry was present in the very simplest things which I had previously ignored, never suspecting that they might at any moment, if only one looked close enough at them, turn into a work of art.

How many times had I seen an organ-grinder playing in the street! But only now, when I saw one with Bunin's eyes, did I realize that this organ-grinder was poetry, his monkey was poetry, and the road from Odessa to the Fontan coast was also poetry. 'The villa fences are still arrayed in the acacia's living shade. From behind the villas the sun peeps through the leaves. At every lane the bright sea slowly heaves. . . . The day will be long and light and hot. All things will sleep. The tiles will gleam like glass, and like the soundless sweep of wings a bicycle will pass, and ice will rattle in a German cart.'

It turned out that this was all purest poetry if only, of course, one could disclose the soul of the thing or event one was writing about. For instance, the soul of the bicycle that would pass 'like the soundless sweep of wings.' The accuracy of that sweep of wings, which somehow managed to express also the swish of tyres, literally drove me mad, particularly as it seemed to suggest yet another idea, 'spokes,' with their gleam of nickel-plating and the tiny lightning flashes of reflected sunlight.

On reading what I have written, I find it all seems to be true, and yet not quite. I am oversimplified for a young man of those days. Of this period Alexander Blok was later to write in his preface to *Vengeance*:

'It is interesting and not unrewarding both for oneself and others to recall the history of one's own work. The more so since we, the most fortunate, or unfortunate, children of our age, have to recall our whole lives: every year we have lived is for us vividly coloured and – alas! – not one can be forgotten, because they are all coloured too indelibly, and every number seems to be written in blood; none of us can forget these numbers, for they are written on our own faces.'

The book I am writing now is, in some measure, the history of one of my own works, or rather of a work, a novel, *The Angel of Death*, that all my life I have dreamed of writing but have never written. It has remained forever a dream.

The book of my dreams.

I was a younger contemporary of Blok, but not so young that I did not feel the time as Blok felt it.

'. . . The year 1910,' Blok wrote, 'saw the crisis of symbolism, of which very much was written and said at the time both in the symbolists' camp and in the camp that opposed them. In that year certain trends made themselves felt that assumed positions hostile to symbolism and to one another: acmeism, egofuturism, and the first beginnings of futurism.'

What 1910 was for Blok, the years 1913 and 1914 were for us young provincials, when those 'first beginnings of futurism' eventually reached Odessa in the shape of strange little books printed on something almost as thick as wrapping paper with bits of wood in it, unusual type, strange titles like A *Slap in the Face to Public Opinion*, *The Carrion Moon*

31

and even *The Sugared Rat*, incomprehensible verses, and the outlandish names of futurist poets, which seemed deliberately devised to tease their readers.

We hid these volumes under our desks together with the subversive *Satirikon* and the indecent adventures of a certain Elsa Gavronskaya in which everything was, in fact, perfectly decent and sickeningly tedious, though it was considered pornography by the directors of the gymnasium.

Among these poems of which I could not understand a word, printed at all angles across the page, and sometimes even upside down, which was considered to be a very bold piece of mystification and even an ominous sort of protest – '*Dyr bul shchyl – ubeshchur*'[1] – I came across a futurist collection called A *Stew of Judges*, a firm square book bound in flowered wallpaper and printed on thick blue sheets that were almost like cardboard, where I found the following lines: 'In the ears of deafened steamers the ear-rings of anchors gleamed.'

And suddenly I, brought up on the classics and now just beginning to understand Bunin's magical realism, read these futurist lines and saw an astonishingly vivid image of a port and heard the familiar roar of a ship's siren, so deep and penetratingly powerful that as soon as it sounded, releasing a hose-jet of transparently heated steam that took some minutes to become a thick cloud overhead, sprinkling rain on the heads and faces of the passengers, who stuck their fingers in their ears in horror and opened their mouths wide to save their eardrums, complete stillness reigned in the world. The blast of a ship's siren always carried the association of sudden silence in the roads and complete and crushing deafness.

I realized that the deafened steamers were by no means a piece of futurist fussiness but an astonishingly true realistic portrayal. We called it 'inversion,' and in those days it was a completely new device, a poetic discovery – the transfer of

[1] Pure sound effects with no meaning.

the sense of deafness from the person to the thing. The ships became living beings, iron women with anchors for ear-rings in their deafened ears.

As for the love and lust (in a later variant) which they howled from their 'brass funnels,' this was a poet's brilliant insight into the depths of the subconscious: when the ship's siren hooted it really did evoke something like a sexual feeling that sent a great tremor of expectation through the whole harbour with its customs launches, tugs, barges, boats, flags, and white lighthouse, whose reflection scattered like the scraps of a torn letter in the blue mirror of the water, with tattered shreds of seagulls, with the anticipation of a sultry seaside night.

I did not even remember the name of the futurist who had written those lines, but the image of the port created by his powerful imagination remained carved in my memory along with Bunin's comparison of a seagull to a fisherman's float.

While I waited for a fresh meeting with Bunin I went over in my mind for the hundredth time the details of that un-forgettable day when he made his first pencil marks in my exercise-book and advised me to read more books about the history of the peoples inhabiting the globe. A real poet, he said, must be well read in the history of world civilization. The life, the customs, the scenery of various countries, their religions, beliefs, folk songs, legends and sagas. In those days – alas! – none of those things excited me although I pre-tended to be delighted with his wise advice and made a great show of taking down the titles of books he recommended.

What I wanted to read was something that would teach me at once and without much trouble how to write marvel-lous verses and become a famous poet.

I was also disappointed by Bunin's insistent advice not to rush into print, but to go about it at my own pace, because everything would come in time.

'I have no doubt,' Bunin remarked at this point with a dry half-smile, 'that you will ignore my advice. You will send your poems to all sorts of publishers just for the sake of seeing them and, above all, your own name in print. I have been through all that myself. And now I regret that I printed a great deal of weak stuff. After all it would cost me nothing to give you my card and you would be published in any of the big monthlies. . . .'

Goodness, even in the *Sovremenni Mir*? I thought dazedly.

'. . . but better not. Wait a while.'

How I longed to plead with him.
'Oh, please, please, Ivan Alexeyevich, recommend my poems, please give me your card. Why not? You say yourself it would cost you nothing.'
But with false humility I agreed with him.
'Yes, I quite understand. Yes, of course, you're quite right. I had better wait.'
He looked at me sarcastically.
'I suppose you will go straight to the *Odessa Bulletin* with your poems today. I know you young poets! You can't fool me. I was the same myself once.'
Then he changed the subject.
'You, of course, want to find out from me as quick as you can all the secrets of writing,' he said very seriously, with deep conviction. 'I don't know whether I can help you. But remember the following. First of all, and above all, you must overcome the tendency to recoil from a clean sheet of paper that nearly every real writer experiences. You must write every day, regularly, without waiting for inspiration, the right mood and so on. You must write in the same way as you would go to work—or to school.'

Now I waited feverishly for each new meeting with Bunin, but just then the war broke out. He went away and I did not see him again until four years later, when we met on the steps of the spiral staircase that led down into the basement office of the *Odessa Bulletin*, where I was collecting a fee for some verse of mine the paper had published.

He stood before me, as dry, bilious, metropolitan and aloof as ever, the same Iv. Bunin of whom through all these years – even on duty at an artillery observation post – I had never ceased to think, and who had become a kind of monitor of my artistic consciousness. Stepping back a pace, he silently examined me in every detail, as though he intended to describe me on the spot.

'Do you recognize me?' I asked.

He made no reply – for a moment it seemed to me that he had not heard my question – and went on examining me, I should say *reading* me, and even making occasional mental notes in the margin.

'Officer. St George Cross. Demobilized. Grown up, much more mature.' He glanced at my right leg, which I could still not put very firmly on the step. 'Wounded. But no damage to the bone, I think?'

As usual I began to cough from embarrassment. He pricked up his ears, listening to my harsh coughing, which was much deeper than before.

'Gas?' he asked tentatively. 'Phosgene?' And then he offered me his familiar dry hand, the palm frankly open and friendly. 'Hullo, Valya,' he said, and I felt he was admiring me. 'The young poet Valentin Katayev!'

'Have you been in Odessa long?'

I asked the question out of embarrassment because I already knew of his flight from Bolshevik Moscow to Odessa, where he had recently published several new poems of which I then knew nothing, except that one of them was a description of a poetry evening, probably a Moscow one, and of a woman poet I had never heard of.

'A big muff. A palid cheek. . . .'

Then, if I remembered rightly, this poetess said languidly:

'Kuzmin, do read your new triolet.'

And the whole poem, which was not very long, ended with the brief line:

'Boring, sexless and dissolute.'

Here was all Bunin, his precision, laconicism, spleen and hatred of dilettante art.

I remarked that the poet Kuzmin had never to my knowledge written any triolets. Bunin said he had not been referring to Mikhail Kuzmin. He used the first name that came into his head. 'I can change it to something else, if you like.'

From one of the other poems I can remember two fragments. The first:

'Where are you now? Do you delight in the waves of green Biscay 'mid panamas and dresses white?'

And the last:

'Pray give my respects to the Prince and Princess. Your youthful hand I kiss in pride with love that henceforth I no longer hide.'

I have never found these poems in any collection but I think that if one searched the Odessa papers and magazines of those days they would turn up.

This was for me a new and frightening Bunin, almost an emigré or, perhaps, already wholly an emigré, who sensed completely and to the bottom of his soul the collapse and destruction of the old Russia, the severing of all former ties. Only a man who had realized to the full that life was finished, that this was the end, could have written, could have publicly and in print declared his secret, tender and perhaps even illicit love which 'henceforth I no longer hide.'

Why henceforth? Why should he no longer hide it?

Because it was all over. This was the end. He had stayed behind in a Russia that was in the grip of a ruthless and, for him, terrible revolution. She – a young princess – was already far away in France, on the shores of 'green Biscay 'mid panamas and dresses white.'

And then, instead of just 'give' there was that old-fashioned and elegant 'pray give' used only in high society.

'Pray give my respects to the Prince and Princess.'

I felt something tragic in these lines. Despair. Horror. Resignation. They were the kind of lines one might have written the night before going to the scaffold.

We walked down Lanzheronovskaya Street past the municipal theatre, past the lawn on which the Odessa coat-of-arms was laid out in flowers, past the classical portico of the History Museum, past the city duma, past the famous iron cannon on its stepped wooden gun-carriage. Then we walked on unhurriedly down the Nikolayevsky Boulevard from the Pushkin monument in the direction of the statue of the Duc de Richelieu with the iron bomb embedded in the socle and his arm pointing out to sea.

The palace near the London Hotel had been taken over by the Germans for their headquarters. There were pairs of sentries in capacious grey steel helmets at the entrance. High across the boulevard hung a bright-yellow, I'd say wasp-yellow, streamer with a very clearly inscribed black Gothic inscription on it, which Bunin paused to read with his keen, long-sighted eyes: 'Automobilenlangsamfahren! – Motor vehicles drive slowly.'

Two or three Austrian officers with sabres in nickel-plated sheaths were standing in front of the headquarters building, reading the long typed and mimeographed communiqués signed by Field-Marshal von Ludendorff that were pinned up in wire-fronted cases.

How strange it was for me, a Russian officer, decorated with the Cross of St George, to be walking about a Russian town occupied by the enemy in the company of a Russian Academician, a famous writer, who had of his own free will fled from Soviet Russia, giving way to the general panic and escaping from no one knew what to the enemy-occupied south, to a Ukrainian State created by the Germans and ruled by the previously quite unknown Hetman Skoropadsky, an operettish figure, once a general or perhaps only a colonel in the former tsarist army.

'When did we last see each other?' Bunin asked.

'In the July of 'fourteen.'

'The July of 'fourteen,' he said thoughtfully. 'Four years. War. Revolution. An eternity.'

'I called again at your villa but found nobody there.'

'Yes, I left for Moscow the day after the declaration of war. I had the greatest difficulty in getting away. Everywhere was jammed with troop trains. I was afraid of Rumania, the Turkish Navy. . . .'

We were both silent.

I had a vision of a blazing July day. A powerful dry wind from the steppes driving clouds of black dust and wads of pressed hay across the Kulikovo Field and flicking up the tails of the horses that had been commandeered in the surrounding villages, and the sky of a menacing metallic hue and the blood-red sunset that remained forever connected in my mind with the lines:

' "Evening edition! Italy! Germany! Austria! Declare war!" And on the sombre, black-edged square a stream of blood ran red.'

And with others even more terrifying: 'Mother and an evening killed by Germans. Oh, close, close those newspaper eyes!'

They had been written fearlessly at a time of wild patriotic fervour by that same young futurist poet, whose poem *The Port* had so delighted me. But by now I knew his name: Vladimir Mayakovsky.

'A ring at the bell. What is it, mother? You're white, white as a coffin shroud. Stop it! It's about him, a telegram to say he's dead. Oh, close, close those newspaper eyes!'

Those lines had been in my heart all through the war. But what could Bunin know of that? In his presence I was afraid even to utter the blasphemous name of Mayakovsky. In the same way, incidentally, as I was later never able in Maya-kovsky's presence to mention Bunin. The one automatically excluded the other.

But they both stand side by side in my memory and there is nothing I can do about it.

Bunin walked fast, his sharp little beard jutting out, his sinewy neck twisting this way and that, as though he were bent on remembering and then describing most precisely all that was going on around : the blotchy pistachio-green trunks of the centenarian plane trees, the petrified port below the boulevard, the long Benz limousine from the German Headquarters, sweeping over the asphalt past the policeman on the corner, who was just an ordinary Russian soldier with a round official cockade on his cap, embellished with an odd sort of trident intended to mark the soldier's allegiance to Hetman Skoropadsky's so-called 'guard of state.'

The familiar striped awnings of the fruit stalls in Cathe-rine's Square, where there were bast baskets full of early strawberries – big, dry ones – and almost black or pale-pink cherries, whose mirror-like skins reflected the now almost summer sun.

But in the resolutely clenched jaws and intently concen-trated face of my teacher I noticed a well-concealed embar-rassment, even confusion. I learned that he had come here with his wife, was staying in town with the artist Bukovet-sky, but would soon be moving out to a villa, where he invited me to visit him.

Thus began my two years' acquaintance with Bunin, which lasted right up to the day when finally and forever he left the land of his birth.

Once again a villa at the Sixteenth Station. But this time it was not Kovalevsky's villa, where I had first set eyes upon him. It was another villa, before you got to Kovalevsky's, to the right of the tram lines. Closer to the steppe than to the sea. But just as typical of the Bolshoi Fontan coast – a limestone house with a tiled roof, a border full of Marvel-of-Peru, roses, Persian lilac, and arbor vitae, dry, dusty, almost black, with light-blue fleshy turpentine-smelling bumps on their lacy branches and always a white mist of cobwebs hovering in their depths. The open veranda was so densely overgrown with wild vines that when you entered by the sun-warmed steps from the blazing light of the steppe you were at first blinded by the darkness until there emerged from the golden gloom a dinner table covered with flowered oil-cloth with pinkish cocoa stains on it and wasps crawling over them.

It was on that kind of veranda that I first met Bunin's wife – Vera Nikolayevna Muromtseva, a beautiful young woman – not a great lady but most emphatically a woman – very tall, with a cameo face, her hair combed back and falling in a knot on the nape of her neck, blue-eyed, dressed like a girl student, one of those unobtrusive Moscow beauties from an intellectual, professorial environment, which had always seemed to me even more inaccessible than, for example, the thick monthly journal in a brick-red cover with its title *European Herald* printed across it in old Cyrillic script, which came out under the editorship of a professor with the significant, impressive and very scholarly sounding name of Ovsyaniko-Kulikovsky.

In the abstract I realized that Vera Nikolayevna was beautiful, but she was not to my taste – those large feet in button-across shoes, the rather long nose of a classical goddess – Demeter, for instance – virtuous, but, above all, the wife of Bunin, though not even married to him in church, but in the liberal Moscow style, only at a registry office, of which in his autobiographical note Bunin, who, I believe, had been married before, wrote that from a certain year 'my life has been shared by V. N. Muromtseva.'

She was the niece of the president of the First State Duma, a leading bourgeois politician in Moscow constitutional democratic circles, the inspirer and organizer of the famous Vyborg Appeal.

Now Bunin and his wife, having both fled from the Bolsheviks, or as the current phrase had it – from Sovdepland – were staying at a villa with some other refugees from Moscow, waiting for the day when Soviet rule would eventually collapse and they could go back home.

I became so frequent a guest at their house that Bunin, quite unrestrained by my presence, would sometimes quarrel with his wife in the Moscow style.

'Vera, you are an utter fool!' he would shout irritably.

And she would gaze at him with her submissively loving, angelic blue eyes and reply mournfully:

'Ioann, I implore you not to be so unbearably rude.' And as she wrung her long bluish fingers: 'Do stop raving! What will this young poet think of us? It may appear to him that you don't respect me.'

I remember how extremely surprised I was by that mannered 'Ioann' in reference to Bunin. But I soon realized that this was quite in the spirit of the Moscow of those days, where it was very much the fashion to be interested in Russia's distant past. To call one's husband Ioann, instead of Ivan, was quite in the Moscow style and could possibly have been an allusion to Ioann the Terrible with his dry bilious face, his short beard, seven wives and that royal narrowing of his eagle eyes.

In any case it was quite obvious that Vera Nikolayevna experienced before her lord and master, who was not really at all like Ivan, or Ioann, the Terrible, a fluttering of the heart and, perhaps, even the adoration of the loyal subject.

Before ancient Russia came into fashion she had, I believe, been in the habit of calling Bunin after the Polish manner: Jan.

I kept bringing my Mentor more and more new poems and stories.

'Look at this, Vera,' Bunin would say, holding up my compositions and nodding at me. 'Like all beginners, he imagines that writing will bring him fame, money and a life of luxury. Confess, my good sir,' he said, now addressing me directly, 'that you dream of seeing your photograph in the magazines and newspapers, of enthusiastic press notices. You have visions of a villa in Finland, a current account with the Credit Lyonnaise, a beautiful wife, a car! Look at him blushing, Vera! Now he will lie to us that he desires none of these things, that he desires only pure art. But let me tell you this, sir. Don't imagine that all famous writers are bound to be rich. Before providing themselves with even a modest livelihood – very modest indeed! – nearly all of them have experienced horrifying poverty, almost beggary. You don't believe me? Well, tell me, how do you picture Kuprin, for instance? He's a famous writer, isn't he? He's published everywhere, he has a tremendous reputation, he's the idol of the reading public. You agree, do you not?'

'Of course.'

'Very well. Then let me tell you that in the life of this famous writer Kuprin there have been months when he has not had as much as three kopecks to his name. Not figuratively speaking, but literally, three copper kopecks.'

Bunin uttered these words so expressively that I could almost see on his outstretched palm one of those copper coins with its blackened eagle – the tsarist three-kopeck piece – which had by then practically disappeared from circulation, like all the other tsarist small change, having been replaced by postage stamps – blue ten-kopeck ones and green ones for twenty kopecks and queer yellow fifty-kopeck notes issued by the Odessa municipal council with the city's coat-of-arms on them in the shape of a heraldic shield and a black anchor; and one had to stuff one's purse with all these tattered bits of paper instead of coins.

Bunin would take my manuscripts off to his room, then come back to the veranda after a time and say: 'Well, carry on. You are getting somewhere, but you have a lot of work to do yet.'

Or something of that kind.

At home I would scrutinize the marks left by his pencil or fingernail, the light underlinings, the notabenes, the ticks and crosses, the exclamation marks, and rack my brains over their meaning.

'Here the mysterious fingernail of riddle hath passed. . . .'

I awaited our next meeting with an impatience that drove me to the point of real madness.

One could not appear in the morning because he was working. I used to come out from town after dinner, towards evening. And sometimes, if I had no stamps for the tram fare, I would walk, covering fifteen versts or so along the dusty Bolshoi Fontan Road, past villas, beacons and stations, stopping now and then to admire the open sea with its snow-white crests from which such a clean free wind was blowing.

The sun would be setting over the steppe and the shadows of my legs in their boots and army breeches – so long that I seemed to be walking on stilts – reached the wormwood-fringed edge of the cliff, and then broke off, so that the shadow of my body and head in its crumpled front-line cap seemed to plunge away into the abyss, like some astral body, only occasionally materializing as a tiny silhouette on the pebble beach or on the turbid green waves, twisted like a refractory glass tube and suddenly dashed to pieces among the rocks.

With the persistence of a maniac I thought about Bunin, about his new poems and prose, which he had brought from Soviet Russia, from mysterious revolutionary Moscow.

This was a different Bunin, as yet unknown to me, a new person compared with the one I knew inside out from his collected works, which had appeared as a supplement to the magazine *Niva* during the war, in a yellow cover with a handsome vignette composed of wind-driven leaves.

He was apparently still regarded as a bard of autumn, the author of *Falling Leaves*, which I had never ceased to admire.

'The forest, like a painted tower, in purple, gold and violet shades, rears its gaily coloured wall above the gleam-lit glades.'

Just as *Evgeni Onegin* was considered an encyclopaedia of Russian life, this quite short descriptive poem seemed to me an encyclopaedia of the autumn scenes of all Russian poetry, from Derzhavin to Fet and Polonsky.

Perhaps there was nothing new in it, but *Falling Leaves* brilliantly summed up a whole poetic epoch. Each line evoked associations that are dear to every Russian.

'Autumn, a saddened widow now, enters her pretty tower. . . .' '. . . Then does the slow moon rise, all shadows shorten, spread a lucid haze across the woods and gaze straight in her eyes from the misty heights of heaven.'

Here I would always remember Pushkin's: 'Soft as a ghost the misty moon beyond the pinewood rose.'

The lines: 'In distant fields the bugles blow; their harmonies of bronze ring forth,' brought to mind *Count Nulin*.

Yet at the same time it was all Bunin, all completely original: 'then Autumn in ermine cape and hood, her pale face washed to meet the dying wood, stepped forth. . . .'

And then the superb culmination: 'With crystal and silver in azure skies ice palaces will glow. At night amid these chambers white the lights of heaven will rise, and the Pleiades' starry shield return while midst the frosty stillness burn Aurora's fires.'

There was something impressive in the way the word 'Autumn' was written with a capital letter, like a proper noun. In those days it delighted me. Now it strikes me as mannered. Still, the poetry was wonderful.

In his early days Bunin was still captivated by the traditionalist, populist ideas of his country as a land of poverty, submission and wretchedness.

'I love not, Russia, your thousand years of timid, servile poverty. And yet, this cross, this whitened wooden ladle, are features dear and meek.'

44

He was then still charmed by poverty-stricken Russia, just as another poet, his contemporary, was charmed:

'Russia, land of poverty, your grey log huts, your wind-borne songs are love's first tears to me.'

But now, in the last book of Bunin's verse to be published in pre-revolutionary Russia, the last volume of his collected works, put out by the then little known Parus Publishers in 1918, I read a poem, *The Archistrategus*, in which Bunin pictures Russia quite differently:

'The Archistrategus of the Middle Ages, painted centuries ago upon a single-domed church, was slim-legged, winged, steel-clad from head to toe. Who knew him? But in recent years at fashion's strutting whim a discovery is made. And lo! in a sumptuous journal he appears, displayed for all to see. And now the mystics, god-seekers, aesthetes, poets, every simpering miss holds forth. Their bloated, blathering lips proclaim Russia the Archistrategus, profane the rags of Christ, and gain – from books – the passion to declare how meek and simple Russia is.'

Bunin wrote this poem, I believe, in 1916, with a prophetic sense of the approaching revolution that he feared so much, and to which he was never able to reconcile himself.

Later, as an emigré, towards the end of his life, Bunin deleted the mystics, god-seekers, poets and aesthetes; he also deleted 'their bloated, blathering lips.' But I do not accept this self-censorship. What is written is written. What is said cannot be unsaid.

So was there revealed to me a new Bunin, one that seemed to have emerged from the hereafter, from the world of ancient Russia, cruel, fantastic, unlike anything else, and yet profoundly national and dear to us, the world of our ancestors who created Russia in their own image with all its monstrous mixture of heathen and Christian, old Slavonic and Ugro-Finnic, Varangian, Byzantian, Tatar – cruel, bloody, brilliantly original! – a realm not in the least like the 'ancient Rus' that we had come to imagine from the wretched, thin textbook of Russian history we read in the junior classes at school.

It is enough to enumerate the titles of Bunin's poems of this period: *The Horde, The Six-Winged, The Buffoons, The Execution, The Black Monk, Mathew the Percipient*, to understand what was going on in Bunin's heart at that time.

'In Batu's flames you blazed red and sombre grew your awful gaze. In sacred trepidation red-gold wings you spread. The Terrible's, the God-fool's monkish cowl you once perceived, and forever was your great-eyed visage in vaulted ceiling cleaved.'

His almost incoherent lines of that period still disturb me deeply:

'May one winter fiercer be than all the rest. . . . His crabbed face in laughter creased, and from his mouth blinked blackened teeth. . . .' 'Misty, misty is the reddening morn. . . . Sharpen the knife and soak the lash in brine! . . . Come, fellow, let me wash my face and put on boots and coat, then lead me out and stab me at a stroke – if not, beware! My teeth shall tear you all and from none be torn!' 'Prince Vyacheslav in irons was fettered. . . .' 'My cave is cool and dark. . . . My clothes are rags. . . . A coffin is my bed at night. . . . Oh, Lord! My faith revive and gird me for the fight!'

If a poet's verses bear some resemblance to his soul, as undoubtedly they do, assuming him to be a real poet, the soul of Bunin, the Bunin I walked along the Bolshoi Fontan shore to see, was writhing in the flames of hell, and if he did not groan it was only because he still hoped the Revolution was near its end.

Meanwhile life went on and at times it even began to appear that nothing very much had happened. Simply that, as in past years, people had come to spend the summer in the south, on the Odessa coast. They were not refugees, not emigrés. They were just ordinary summer residents with their blue enamel saucepans, Gretz oil stoves, bathing caps, bicycles, sandals, croquet mallets. . . . There may have been far more of them than usual, but even this gave no particular cause for alarm. It might have been just a good summer with fine weather and, as the *Odessa Bulletin* put it, the holiday season was in full swing and the 'influx' of summer visitors was so large that villas were being shared by two or three families.

The Bunins, for instance, were sharing a villa with a very rich and corpulent lady who was a writer and had just had something published in the *European Herald*, which in those days was equivalent to 'entering literature on the grand scale.' The lady and her family – a plump little daughter and a quite unremarkable but perfectly polite well-to-do civil servant husband – willingly made room for Bunin, whose fame in recent years had noticeably increased, and gave him two rooms and a veranda. Bunin was now not only the poet of solitude, bard of the Russian countryside and the impoverished gentry, he was also the author of those amazingly original and powerful stories, *The Gentleman from San Francisco*, *The Dreams of Chang* and *Light Breathing*, which had at once made him almost the leading prose writer in Russia.

Even my friends – the young and not so young poets of Odessa – one fine day, as though by word of command, proclaimed him to be an incontrovertible authority; the magazine *Niva* had given its readers Bunin's collected works as a supplement, and this had at once made him a classic.

Bunin had the appearance of a summer visitor, but not the banal, provincial type in straw hat, apache shirt and canvas shoes. Bunin was a visitor from the metropolis, exquisitely intellectual, in expensive summer sandals, foreign socks and a flowing well-ironed shirt of unbleached linen with a turned-down collar and a folded pair of steel-rimmed pince-nez in the small breast pocket; the shirt was girdled not with a cheap silk cord with frayed tassels – like my father's, for example – but with a plain but evidently rather expensive leather belt, into which he sometimes tucked his hands rather after the manner of Tolstoy; he wore no hat, but if the sun was very hot he would suddenly appear in a splendid real panama hat, brought back from some distant land, or else a linen peaked cap of the kind that used to be worn in summer by Fet, Polonsky or perhaps even Tolstoy himself.

I see a large company on the veranda. Actually I cannot see it. I force myself to see it, groping in darkness round the mysterious mechanism of memory and feeling its innermost complexes with calloused fingers.

All these people are refugees from Soviet Russia: eminent barristers, doctors, writers, even Academician Ovsyaniko-Kulikovsky himself, the famous author of *The Psychology of Creativity* and articles on Turgenev, the editor of that most unattainable and respected journal the *European Herald*, which quite recently published the little story by the stout lady who has let half the villa to the Bunins. Now she has really 'entered Russian literature' and feels perfectly at home there.

I, for example, have not yet entered those sacred portals, but she has!

She was not only stout. She was massive, forceful, with prominent cheeks and round muscles at the sides of her small mouth. With a firm apple chin. Black-haired, black-browed, hot-cheeked, energetic, and yet at the same time so demurely, in a purely feminine way, melting between the two famous Academicians.

Never before had Odessa attracted such brilliant society. True, they were all refugees, political emigrés, flotsam, but all the same! . . .

Anyhow, who can say?

Bunin is in a splendid, rather sarcastic mood. He glances sideways at the forceful corpulent lady, as though listening to the silky crackle of her corset. He might almost be about to take out his pen and describe her on the spot. Not just a general description but the perfect definition, given at one stroke. I can see him searching for that one, perfectly accurate word, and at the same time I realize he is secretly giving me a lesson in the art of writing.

Presently I can tell from his face that he has found what he wants, and that his find is unique and precious. He makes a faint gesture, as though to enclose from a distance the stout lady's face in a magical, musical oval.

Everyone stops talking to hear what he will say.

'Yes, indeed,' he says, planting with his forefinger two commas tail upwards in the oval he has just drawn. 'All you need, Elena Vasilyevna, is a little black moustache and you would be the image of – Peter the Great.'

And we all suddenly saw Peter's face.

The lady blushes purple, not knowing how to take the comparison. On the one hand, something regal has been detected in her face, which is a good thing, particularly in these troubled revolutionary times; on the other hand, there is a suggestion of something masculine, which is bad. However, what really matters is that she has been 'described' by the famous Bunin in the presence of the famous Ovsyaniko-Kulikovsky, and this resolves all her doubts.

She smiles at Bunin femininely and at the same time regally, and, just to be on the safe side, wags a finger at him.

'Really, Ivan Alexeyevich, how can you pay such compliments in public!'

I stored the incident away in my mind, generalizing Bunin's discovery as 'the feminine face of Peter.'

One day I, too, was caught in the field of his diabolic vision. He looked at me suddenly and made certain intricate signs in the air on a level with my head.

'Look, Vera,' he said. 'His ears are perfectly wolfish. And in general, sir,' he said, addressing me severely, 'there is something extremely wolfish about you.'

. . . Bunin himself had wolfish ears and I had noticed them even before he noticed mine.

A sad, golden day at the end of summer. We spent it

together, alone in the empty villa; our neighbours had moved back to the city and Vera Nikolayevna had gone off by tram to the city market to bring back supplies, which were becoming more and more difficult to obtain.

The day before, I had brought Bunin – at his demand – everything I had so far written: about thirty poems and several stories, some of them in manuscript, others in the form of clippings from newspapers and magazines pasted on sheets of office paper. It made quite an impressive bundle.

'Come over tomorrow morning and we'll have a talk,' Bunin said.

I duly arrived and sat on the steps, waiting for him to come out. He came out and sat down beside me. It was the first time I had seen him so quiet and thoughtful. He was silent for a time, then he said – with unhurried concentration – something that I have not forgotten to this day, and added: 'I mean what I say.'

I dared not believe my ears. Nothing seemed real any more. He said nothing for a while, then leaned forward and, staring intently at a small sea shell amid the gravel, suddenly began to recite poems that were as yet unknown to me. I had never heard him reading his own verse. He spoke it as though talking to himself, mumbling a little, and breathing in deeply during pauses or caesuras:

'My Night will come, a Darkness long and dumb. Then God, who wonders did devise, shall make a new star rise. Shine on, shine on, oh Moon, lift up your Sun-begotten face, and be it known to the world: my Day is spent but not without a trace.'

And then he read another poem:

'With stars my sail is spun, tall, white and taut. The Virgin's face between them shines, serene and still. What care I that the shore from me recedes! My soul is full, my soul is stern. And finely gleams the crescent moon as darkness falls.'

I took this day to be the day of my initiation as an

apprentice, or, perhaps, even as an assistant to the master.

Memory has not retained the details of our conversation. Perhaps nothing was said. Perhaps there was only a long silence. It was a sad, golden autumn day, the sea was dead calm and in the sky there hung a pallid half-grown moon, like a small white cloud.

The Bunin that sat beside me on the steps in a linen blouse was not at all the unpleasantly bilious, dry and haughty person he was generally considered to be. That day for an instant his soul – sad, very lonely, easily wounded, independent, fearless and yet surprisingly tender – was revealed to me.

I remember being astonished that this Bunin, this child of fortune – as he then seemed to me – should be so deeply dissatisfied with his position in literature, or rather, his position in relation to the writers who were his contemporaries.

It was true, of course, that for the wider public he did not stand out from among the noisy crowd of what he bitterly called the 'literary bazaar.' He was overshadowed by stars of the first magnitude, whose names were on every lip: Korolenko, Kuprin, Gorky, Leonid Andreyev, Merezhkovsky, Fyodor Sologub, and many other 'masters of men's minds.'

He was not a master of minds.

Poetry was ruled by Alexander Blok, Balmont, Bryusov, Zinaida Gippius, Gumilyov, Akhmatova and, finally, whether they liked it or not – Igor Severyanin, whose name was known not only to every student and young officer but also to many shop assistants, district nurses, commercial travellers and officer cadets who had not the slightest idea at the time that there was such a Russian writer as Ivan Bunin.

Bunin had been known and appreciated – at least, until quite recently – by a very small number of students and connoisseurs of Russian literature, who realized that he was writing much better than any of his contemporaries. The

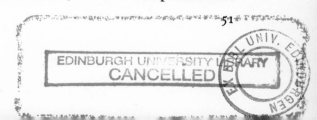

critics, particularly in the early stages of his career, wrote little and rarely about Bunin because his work offered no material for 'problem' articles or pretexts for literary fireworks. For the same reason his name did not figure on the notices announcing public lectures and debates, where the third-rate Artsybashev with his sex problems reigned supreme.

He did not speak to me directly of all this, but these were the thoughts implied in his sporadic remarks about contemporary literature, which were full of venom and sarcasm.

One could have drawn the conclusion that out of all contemporary Russian literature he unconditionally acknowledged only Leo Tolstoy as his superior. Chekhov he considered a writer on his own level, so to speak, perhaps a little higher – but very little. As for the rest. . . What were the rest? Kuprin was gifted, very gifted, in fact, but often careless. Of Leonid Andreyev Tolstoy had aptly remarked : 'He tries to frighten us, but I am not frightened.' Gorky and Korolenko were not really artists but journalists, which did not detract from their great talents, but . . . real poetry had degenerated. Balmont, Bryusov, Bely were nothing more than a Moscow-bred crowd of decadents, a mixture of French and Nizhny-Novgorod vernacular. 'Oh, cover your pale legs,' 'I want to be brash, I want to be bold, I want to tear off your dress,' 'He laughed in a thunderous bass and sent pineapples into space,' and similar nonsense; Akhmatova was a provincial young lady in the big city; Alexander Blok was farfetched, bookish German poetry; the servile 'poesies' of Igor Severyanin – how could anyone ever have invented such a revolting word ! – were not worth talking about; and the futurists were simply criminal types, runaway convicts. . . .

On the whole, Bunin repeated, though in slightly different terms, approximately what he had said several years before in his speech at the jubilee of the *Russian News* :

'. . . what have we not done with our literature in recent years, what have we not mimicked, what have we not imitated, from what styles and epochs have we not borrowed, to what gods have we not bowed down! Literally every winter has brought us a new idol. We have experienced decadence, symbolism, neonaturalism, pornography – styled a solution to the sex problem – godfighting, mythmaking, a kind of mystical anarchism, Dionysius and Apollo, "stages to eternity," sadism, snobism, "acceptance of the world" and "non-acceptance of the world," cheap imitations of the Russian style, Adamism, acmeism – and now we have sunk to the tritest type of hooliganism, named by the ridiculous word "futurism." Is this not a Walpurgis night!'

These and similar ideas were what Bunin talked to me about on the steps of the veranda.

All the time he was somehow unusually quiet, thoughtful, inwardly stern and at the same time sorrowfully tender, like a person experiencing some irredeemable spiritual loss.

He was like a man who had lost a great deal of blood. . . .

I believe it was the feeling of losing one's country.

Dinnertime came round and Vera Nikolayevna had still not returned. Beckoning me conspiratorially, Bunin tiptoed stealthily through the villa into the kitchen and, after clattering around there with some metal pots and pans, soon returned with some cold stuffed cabbage rolls on a frying pan and a saucepan of stewed fruit, and with a big hunk of unleavened bread under his arm. He set all this out on the dinner table and commanded me to sit down.

I had never before eaten at the Bunins'. They were not remarkable for their hospitality; in fact, they were rather mean. I believe they did not even have a cook. Instead they ate with their neighbours. Sometimes they took me in there with them for company to have tea or supper with a large gathering of Moscow refugees, where I met many famous people. There Bunin would not hesitate to heap my plate with all sorts of food.

'Don't be shy,' he would say. 'I know you have a wolfish

appetite. Eat well. Nourish yourself. Your young organism needs a lot of food. Poetry and the young ladies drain your strength every day. Don't deny it. I was young myself – I know!'

If there was on the table any wine that had been bought in common, Bunin would take complete possession of one bottle of red and the rest could please themselves. He would appoint me, as the youngest, president of the table and wine-pourer, so that before I made friends with Alexei Tolstoy, for instance, I had poured him more than one glass of wine.

But let us return to the stuffed cabbage.

On the frying pan there were four stuffed cabbage rolls – golden, slightly burned and solidified in fat – and Bunin, having donned his pince-nez, divided them. The two larger ones, with a sidelong glance in my direction, he placed on his own plate, leaving the two smaller ones for me.

'Eat, man, don't be shy. I know you always have a devilish appetite, particularly when you're dining out.'

'What will Vera Nikolayevna say!' I exclaimed.

'She should not be late. Anyway we'll soon finish this off bachelor fashion, take the dishes back to the kitchen – and no one will be any the wiser.'

In those days I really did experience devilish pangs of hunger and I tucked into the appetizing cabbage rolls, wolfing them down like a soldier in the trenches, and taking note of the fact that my host could certainly not be re-proached for lack of appetite either. While he ate, his beard moved carnivorously and faint tremors of pleasure ran down his dry neck, as though accompanying each morsel of cold stuffed cabbage to its proper destination.

When we reached the stewed fruit stage, he said, licking his moustache: 'We won't dirty any more plates. I recommend that we just help ourselves. . . .'

We consumed the stewed fruit straight from the saucepan, the pedantic Bunin having first divided with his spoon – strictly in half – the thick, swollen brew of all kinds of fruits – apricots, plums, cherries, green apples, early pears and so on – and having demanded of me in the sternest tones not to violate the demarcation line, although it was little more than a symbol.

We set to with our spoons, chasing each other as hard as we could go, then lingered while we dipped pieces of the fine white bread into the thick juice and scooped out the divinely sour-sweet dregs and the slippery plum skins.

I don't know why, but it was that saucepan of stewed fruit that somehow brought us together in a very special way. We took the apricot stones with us out into the garden and, sitting on the veranda steps again, cracked them with a brick and, like children, ate the tender white kernels sheathed in coarse skin.

I stayed till late in the evening, or rather, till late at night, and missed the last tram. Bunin walked a little of the way home with me and then we paced back and forth along the Bolshoi Fontan Road, beside the tramlines in front of the villa and sat on the bench outside the gate, and suddenly he began to examine me.

'Before us is the night. How would you describe it in a few words but in such a way that it is *this* night and no other? You see how much of everything there is all round us' – his lean aristocratic head moved in a circle – 'but you must choose only the essential, as they say, the typical. Well?'

Around us there was indeed 'much of everything.'

A few stars, dimmed by the yellow light of the moon. The warm breeze from the steppes. The outlines of the acacia bushes. The fences of the villas. The cries of the quails. The stillness. The distant barking of dogs. Now and then the braying of a donkey. The dusty silver wormwood, its inimitable nocturnal scent. The gleam of the tramlines, which seemed to slide away into the distance, where they turned and were lost in the coal-black darkness. The rustle of a cat or, perhaps, a hedgehog in the dusty sweet-briar bushes. The extinguished beacon.

And how much else besides!

We sat on the bench and while I concentrated desperately on selecting the essential features of the night, Bunin suddenly began to murmur some lines of Fet:

'. . . the gleam of the frozen distance, the scent of the night-time violet. . . .'

He gave a sigh of sorrowful resignation, as though trying to catch some deeper meaning of the verse, then began murmuring afresh:

'. . . a windmill, a nightingale.'

He turned his narrow face towards me, lifted it to the sky and I saw the delight that was written upon it.

' "A windmill, a nightingale," ' he repeated. 'Do you realize how beautiful that is? It could not be better said! He sits there alone in the night, completely overpowered by the love that has taken possession of his soul, unique, inimitable. . . . he sits surrounded by scents, sounds, indefinable visual images, and it is too much for his mind to concentrate on one thing. Now he is carried away by the gleam of the frozen distances; now he can feel nothing but the scent of the night violet; now he hears a windmill drowning the song of the nightingale; now the nightingale's song drowning the noise of the windmill, and this is all part of a love that absorbs everything. "My angel, my distant angel, why do I love you so?" ' he murmured hoarsely, repeating the last line of the poem almost with desperation.

Who will give me back that night!

'Well, sir, how are you going to describe it all?' Bunin said cheerfully.

'I would describe it like this,' I replied. 'That black post holding the tram cable, with its cross-bar like a yoke and the bright moon beside it.'

'Good for you,' Bunin said. 'Just how it should be described.' And again he began murmuring one poem after another, making no pauses or cadences, from Fet's cycle *To Ophelia*: 'Ophelia singing dies, and singing weaves her wreath. With wreaths and songs she glides, then sinks beneath. . . . Days of mad-serene anguish – how soon they all are gone. Long ago did happiness perish, only the songs and wreaths float on. . . .'

Such phrases as 'days of mad-serene anguish' he tried not to say at all, or to say them as quietly as possible, and I realized that here he found them embarrassing, and that what really mattered to him was the 'only the songs and wreaths float on.' He spoke this line with such intense feeling and made such a gentle and effortless gesture, as though sending off those songs and wreaths as they floated away on the river of time into the irretrievable distance.

Then without a pause he began sending off into the distance his own wreaths and songs, entirely new ones which I did not yet know and had perhaps been written only that day:

'. . . This brief life's eternal change shall ever be my consolation – this early sun, smoke from a habitation, in this scarlet park the slow leaves' fall, and you, old bench, I know so well. To future poets whom I know not God will give a secret – remembrance of me; I shall be their dreams, a spirit free of flesh, invulnerable to death, in this scarlet park where all is still. . . .

'. . . A star trembling mid the spheres. . . . Whose wondrous hand this vessel overfull of such a precious dew doth bear? A burning star, chalice of earth's woes, of heaven's tears – why, Lord, didst set me o'er the world to shine throughout the years?'

He spoke softly, as though he wished to impart to me some delectable truth, which had only that moment revealed itself to him:

'In a garden chair,' he murmured, 'on a balcony at night. . . . The sea's lulling murmur. . . . Be trusting, meek and calm, rest from your thoughts. The breezes come and go, breath of the boundless sea. . . . Is there one who guards this sleeping villa's peace? Is there one who measures out our knowledge, our fate, our years? If the heart believes it, it is so. What's within us – that must be. You doze, and on your eyes the soft wind blows gently from above – is this not Love?'

And then again, without a pause:

'Quiet is the villa, dark the night, the blue stars shed a misty light. Sighing, the wide waves stretch away, the blind flowers sway, and often with the breeze, like some spirit clad in aerial flesh, fresh currents of the deep lap over me, sighing in their sleep.'

There were moments when it seemed to me that all these poems were being created this very minute, in my presence, that every line, the waves 'sighing in their sleep,' the 'soft wind' and particularly the brilliant 'blind flowers' (the white tobacco and Marvel-of-Peru) had in some imperceptible way emerged from the reality that surrounded us and become elements of pure poetry.

Magic?

At about eleven in the morning, to escape from the terrible heat of that summer I was sitting in a bath filled to the brim with cold water, into which between long, dead pauses massive drops were falling from the brass tap, striking brief resounding notes in different tones with a kind of monotonous musicality.

Drip! . . . drop! . . . drap! . . . droop! . . .

They acted soothingly, soporifically, shutting off the strange, utterly unprecedented and indefinable reality in which we all lived that summer

It was a few days after the terrible blasts at the artillery dumps, when . . .

Suddenly my father's head appeared round the bathroom

door and I saw from his face that something extraordinary had happened.

'Come out. There's somebody to see you. A strange gentleman. I think it's . . . Bunin.'

When I had pulled on my clothes without having time to dry myself properly, and with my hair still wet had run into the end room, one of the two which we usually let to lodgers and which was now empty, the person I saw was indeed Bunin. Sitting on an upright chair with one leg over the other, he was conversing urbanely with father, who was dressed almost the same as Bunin, except that father's unbleached linen shirt was looser and faded from washing and girdled with a twisted silk girdle with tassels, and his sandals were a cheap pair from the market worn on his bare feet. And compared to Bunin's neatly clipped beard, father's looked somewhat unkempt. However, both father and Bunin, like other Russian intellectuals, had old-fashioned steel-rimmed pince-nez dangling on black cords from their breast pockets, which gave them both a remote resemblance to Chekhov. Bunin a youthful Chekhov, and father an elderly one.

It turned out that I had once mentioned that we were in the habit of letting rooms and Bunin had come over from the Bolshoi Fontan to find accommodation for some of his Moscow refugee friends who had nowhere to live. Later I learned that these refugees were Alexei Tolstoy and his family.

Bunin had already summed up the situation with his usual clear-sightedness and had probably formed an opinion of the way we lived.

I think it must have been similar to the impression that Yuri Olesha in his youth once formed of our flat and of me.

'. . . He liked my verses very much and asked me to read them again and again, roaring his approval. Then he read out his own, which seemed to me the summit of perfection. There was indeed much poignant lyricism in them. . . . I think we were both still at the gymnasium and he received me in a large, rather empty flat, where he lived with his widowed father and brother – a sad, lifeless place with no woman to look after it. . . .'

It was this sad, lifeless flat that Bunin saw, too. Naturally he had realized at once that for Alexei Tolstoy with his lordly ways our rooms with their one sagging couch would not be at all suitable.

Father and Bunin conversed sedately on various subjects. They talked about the explosions at the artillery dumps – Bunin insisted that the Bolsheviks had done it – then went on to household subjects.

Various male accessories – socks, collars, handkerchiefs, which for lack of a maid my father had washed himself in an enamel bowl with a piece of blue-veined Kazan soap – were drying on the hot window-sill of the Venetian window.

'May I offer you some useful advice?' said Bunin. 'Never wash socks in hot water and soap. Rinse them thoroughly in cold water without any soap at all, and don't iron them, just hang them out to dry in the sun. Then your feet will never sweat. I can vouch for that. I learned the method not long ago myself and it has literally restored me to life.'

Having sat there, like an official visitor, for some twenty minutes, having talked about Zhukovsky and Turgenev, and having joined heartily with my father in disapproving of the moderns, Bunin rose, shook hands politely and briefly took his leave.

'Glad to have met you.'

'And how do you find Valya's work?' my father asked almost plaintively, at last overcoming his embarrassment.

'How do you?' Bunin returned the question.

'As his father, it is difficult for me to judge. His poems seem reasonably good as regards rhyme and measure. The stories, I feel, are rather journalistic, unsubstantial and superficial. Do you not find that so?'

'That is a very long and difficult subject to discuss.'

'What do you think – will he make good one day?'

'That is hard to say in a few words,' Bunin replied seriously. 'Time will tell.'

And he left without allowing me to see him off.

Blushing to the roots of my hair, I stood at the half-open door and listened to the sound of his young firm footsteps as he ran downstairs from the third floor, filling the staircase well with boom and clatter.

Only some time later, when I knew Bunin even better, did I realize the true purpose of his visit. The rooms to let were only an excuse. In point of fact – and I am quite convinced of this – Bunin had simply wanted to catch me by surprise and see how I lived, what kind of a flat we had, and who my father was. Bunin was incredibly curious and he always had to know everything, in full detail, about the life around him, and to see everything with his ruthlessly vigilant eyes.

My feelings after Bunin's visit were mixed. On the one hand, it was flattering; on the other, strangely depressing. And suddenly I seemed to see with Bunin's eyes my ageing, lonely father, who had rather let himself slide, with his grey uncut, priestly hair and black unpressed trousers, and our four-room flat, which had always seemed to me so well, even richly furnished, but which was in fact half empty, with its black furniture, cheaply touched up to look like 'ebony' but really only made of deal, as the chipped black and white of the corners and beading manifestly proclaimed; a tasteless style with flower stands in the shape of Doric columns, already contemptuously referred to as 'baro-cuckoo.'

The hanging oil-lamp, its copper bowl filled with buckshot because it had been converted to electricity. Two so-called 'pictures' – provincial oleographs that tried to look like oil paintings, in insultingly narrow gilt frames, which we had hung because we had received them as a free gift from *Niva*, and this related them in some way to the Russian classics, which *Niva* also gave away as its supplement, and which now included Bunin. A once fairly good study couch, reupholstered many times and now covered with cracked and tattered oil-cloth.

And finally the most valuable, even precious, item of all – mother's upright piano, which had been her dowry and was now a battered instrument with shaky pedals, on which father manfully and short-sightedly, peering at the yellowed music and constantly dropping his pince-nez, would uncertainly but with tremendous feeling sometimes play Tchaikovsky's *The Seasons*, always specially repeating *May*, which filled me with an inexpressibly poignant misery.

We were not poor, and certainly not beggars, but there was something that evoked pity in our maladjustment, the lack of a woman – mother and mistress of the house – of any sort of comfort, of curtains on the windows and doors. Everything was naked, bare. . . .

Bunin could not have failed to notice this. He noticed everything. . . .

. . . even the saucepan of cold broth on the window-sill. . . .

When about to leave, he let his eye rest for a moment on my officer's sword, with its red St Anne sword-knot 'for bravery,' which hung forlornly on the empty summer hat-stand, and, so it seemed to me, a pained smile crossed his lips. No wonder. The city was occupied by enemy troops, and here, hung up challengingly for all to see, were the arms of a Russian officer!

He did not know the Austrians had already searched our flat for weapons. I had shown them the sword. The Austrian officer, a young man like myself, all in dark grey, in a perfectly pressed uniform and leather gaiters and a new cap, turned it over in his gloved hands, read out syllable by syllable the inscription 'For bravery,' and returned it to me with a gallant military courtesy, saying that I could keep it because '*such* weapons should not be taken without a fight.'

On the whole, it was all terribly sad.

It was late autumn and there could still be no question of Bunin's returning to Moscow. Soviet rule, for which everyone had predicted immediate collapse, had not only not collapsed, but was even – judging by all the signs – gaining strength.

Revolution had come in Germany. The Kaiser had been deposed, the German Army had surrendered and the Germans and Austrians were hurriedly quitting the Ukraine, so that the conclusion of the obscene Treaty of Brest-Litovsk – which had been the main charge levelled against the Bolsheviks – now had no practical significance: Lenin, it turned out, had been right.

The Germans in Odessa had now been replaced by their conquerors, the 'allies,' and in South Russia there now began a period of almost two years in which power changed hands six times, if not more, until Soviet rule was finally and forever established.

Bunin lived through this unique period of storm and stress in Odessa, on Knyazheskaya Street, in the house of his friend the artist Bukovetsky, who gave him all three rooms on the ground floor, and it was in these rooms that I visited him, always experiencing unbelievable excitement before ringing at the back door.

Usually the door was opened by a very smart maid in French heels, a starched cap and a little cambric apron with dolly pockets. She had been placed at Bunin's disposal along with the rooms and provided a striking contrast to the situation that obtained in the town, in Russia, and in the world.

Bunin's life in these lordly apartments with their massive polished doors, excellently polished parquet, the warm marble sills of the Venetian windows with brightly polished bolts, the high clean ceilings, which in summer reflected the greenery of the white acacias planted all the way along the quiet, exclusive street, and in winter – the blue shadows of the snowdrifts and the washed-out silhouettes of the cab-men's sledges, with only a small quantity of the most essential but very good furniture and none of those petit-bourgeois book-stands, side-cabinets, nick-nacks, doilies, runners, albums, cushion-covers – corresponded as nearly as possible to my conception of an aristocrat, a nobleman, a Russian Academician, a man of irreproachable taste.

Here I saw not a summer visitor but a well-established town-dweller, possibly one who of necessity had become a political recluse, and had evolved a scrupulously exact daily timetable.

He worked a great deal. It was my impression that he worked incessantly. No matter when I called, I always saw the door of his study half open into the shadowy corridor, beyond it a window looking out into a quiet courtyard, a small desk and Bunin, jacketless, in a freshly laundered shirt with the sleeves rolled up to the elbow, exposing his muscular arms, and wearing round spectacles that made him look like an owl, writing rapidly on small narrow sheets of paper in his characteristically compressed cuneiform hand.

He wrote in dark-green ink with a gold-nibbed fountain-pen, manufactured, if I am not mistaken, by the Montblanc pen company. He never blotted the page he had just written, but laid it impatiently aside to dry; if he wrote something in his notebook he would wave it in front of him to dry the page quicker.

On hearing my footsteps, he would usually say, without turning his head: 'Go in to Vera Nikolayevna. I shall finish soon.'

I would walk through to the large room that looked out on Knyazheskaya Street – their drawing-room – where I would be met by Vera Nikolayevna, who in her capacity as mistress of the house would entertain me with light conversation on various subjects without, of course, sinking to that of the weather.

Being a woman of lively intelligence, however, and possessing a curiosity worthy of Bunin himself, she would soon abandon formality and turn the conversation to other matters of a far less formal nature.

'And how is your affair with the charming Natasha N. proceeding? Is she not delightful, with that childishly full mouth and those long arms – a real Natasha Rostova. But mind her mother doesn't turn you out of the house one fine day, for all her gentility. So it's all over with Iren A.? How fickle you are – a real Bunin pupil,' she sighed. 'And may I ask you who it was to whom you dedicated that "someone's tiny feet the marks imprinted"? I just can't guess whose they must be. Are there not rather too many of these little feet?'

She was *au courant* of all my affairs. With some of my girl friends she was personally acquainted and took an extremely lively interest in all my amorous adventures – all of them quite innocent, incidentally! – and far from being the strict wife of an Academician she resembled rather an elder sister or perhaps a married cousin.

'Jan,' she exclaimed to Bunin as he entered the room. 'He is in the throes of a great love affair with Natasha!'

'Of course, he is,' Bunin replied. 'Look at him – hollow cheeks, dark circles under his eyes. Anyone can see that instead of working you have been on the prowl all night. I suppose you stand under her window till dawn, waiting for her to open and let you in. Nothing will come of it, my dear sir, you have picked the wrong woman. I know all about those full-mouthed long-legged school girls!'

Bunin would sit down at a round uncovered table of palisander wood, on which there stood, reflected as in a cherry-red mirror, a copper, or rather, brass bowl stamped with an oriental ornament, which Bunin had probably bought at the Atmeidan bazaar in Constantinople or perhaps in Smyrna or Alexandria.

In any case this bowl reminded me of Bunin's eastern poems and, above all, of course, 'he breathed upon the blade – and before their gaze that Syrian dagger keen was clouded with a bluish haze, but underneath the golden patterns, made in the name of Allah and the Prophet, shone brighter than before. Servant of fate and heaven, tell us your cry of war. Thus he replies: "Grim and terrible is my device. The mystery of mysteries: Alif. Lam. Mim."'

This ash-tray was for me, as it were, the mystery of mysteries: Alif. Lam. Mim. And it was reflected in the round polished table.

Sitting with one leg hooked over the other, Bunin would flick off his cigarette ash into it with great precision.

I don't know why, but I loved that ash-tray. It seemed to me the epitome of luxury, almost a museum piece, an object of mysterious worship, particularly beautiful on the icy surface of the bare, faultlessly polished table, in the middle of this grand drawing-room redolent of expensive Turkish Mesaksudi tobacco with its reverential stillness pro-ʳected from the outside world by double glass doors.

Now I think that ash-tray must have been a very cheap souvenir, of the kind that passengers of the Russian Steamship and Commerce Society brought back in hundreds from their cruises in Asia Minor. But I was simply in love with it and, in a childish way that I had not yet grown out of, thought to myself, 'When I grow up I shall have an ash-tray just like that, and flick ash into it from my Mesaksudi, the very best blend of Turkish tobacco.'

The ash-tray was in those days still quite new and bright, although darkened inside with ash and burned matches, and the very first time I saw it I was for some reason reminded of Bunin's poem *The Censer*.

'In Sicily's hilly lands, in a monastery long forgot, a naked altar stands. And in the dust before it, grave-gilded, long since unlit, of fuel deprived, there lies a censer, all black inside from embers of the resinous wood that once blazed therein. And you, my heart, with fire and fragrance filled, forget it not. Burn, too, until to blackness charred.'

How I dreamed in those days that my heart should burn

till it was charred black! But I never imagined how terrible that could be.

'Well, what is the good news today?'
'I've written a new story.'
'You have brought it with you, of course?'
'Here it is.'
'Vera, don't go away. Valentin Katayev will now read us his latest story. We are listening.'

Usually, having attentively and patiently listened to my story from beginning to end, Bunin would not enter into any detailed discussion. Instead he would restrict himself to two or three brief remarks about what was good or bad in the story, and why one thing was good and the other bad, and what practical conclusions should be drawn from this.

He always touched upon details, but invariably drew important generalizations from them. This was how I learned, for example, that there are no forbidden subjects in literature. What matters is the degree of tact with which they are treated. I at once resolved to be guided always by Bunin's recommendations concerning tact, precision, brevity and simplicity, but, as Bunin often emphasized, he was talking not about that simplicity which, as the saying goes, is worse than robbery, but about the simplicity that comes from intensive work on a phrase or a particular word, about absolutely independent vision of the surrounding world, involving no imitation whatever of anyone, even Tolstoy or Pushkin, in other words, about the ability to see phenomena and things in an entirely individual way and write of them in one's own individual way, free of any literary influences or reminiscences.

He warned me particularly against literary clichés – 'the slanting rays of the setting sun,' 'silence reigned,' 'rain pattered on the window,' and so on, of which Chekhov had spoken even before Bunin.

Among the minor literary clichés Bunin also included, for example, the hack-writer's habit in those days of describing

67

his hero as a 'first-year student,' which seemed to identify the young man and even convey something of his appearance: 'Ivanov, a first-year student, came out of the gate and walked down the street,' 'Sidorov, a first-year student, lighted a cigarette,' 'First-year student Nikanorov felt profoundly miserable.'

'I am sick to death of all these literary first-year students,' Bunin would say.

I at once vowed to myself that no first-year student should ever appear in any story of mine, and to give practical expression to my vow I began that very day to write a story about a young man who was not a student. The result was that I at once found myself stuck. What was the young man to be? Someone older could easily be made into a privy councillor, an army captain, a senior ticket-inspector, all kinds of things. With the old men it was even simpler: general, Counsellor of State, merchant of the second guild, village elder, and so on. But a young man—

I went out for a walk to think in freedom of what I should make my young hero. Almost at once I noticed a theatre bill with a black lyre at the top announcing the first night of some opera or other, on which among other things were printed the words: 'scene-painter Dmitriyev.' Splendid, I thought, my young hero shall be a scene-painter.

And now here I was sitting at the glossy round table with the manuscript of my new story spread out beside the Turkish ash-tray. Coughing with nervousness, I relished in advance Bunin's approval of the fact that my young man was not a first-year student and not even a second lieutenant but – just imagine! – a scene-painter. This sounded *chic*, and was at the same time close to real life.

I read the story very hurriedly and with great fervour. If I remember, it described the young scene-painter's experiences in love, his first rendezvous, the break-up of the affair, a night of debauch, including even the taking of cocaine in some rather suspicious company and, finally, a bright and

68

bitterly cold dawn on the Nikolayevsky Boulevard, with large pink pigeons waddling about on the granite steps of the famous staircase.

I described all this in fine style, all the time casting furtive glances at Bunin to see what impression my prose, which struck me as exceptionally graceful, was making on him.

At first Bunin's withdrawn face expressed his usual professional attentiveness. I actually noticed him exchange a glance with Vera Nikolayevna. Aha, at last I had touched the old man on the raw! But gradually he became more and more sombre, and began impatiently jerking his neck, and by the end of the story – to my horror – he had abandoned any attempt to conceal his irritation and was tapping his heel rather loudly on the parquet floor. When I reached the crowning point with the dawn-pink pigeons, which I had imagined would appeal particularly to Bunin, and not without a certain modest satisfaction uttered the concluding sentence of the story, Bunin said nothing for a time and merely stared at me angrily with terrible, grimly questioning eyes.

'Is that all?' he asked icily.

'Yes,' I said.

'Really! Then why the devil,' he shouted suddenly, banging on the table with his fist with such force that the ash-tray bounced, 'then why the devil have you been leading us up the garden path for the last forty-five minutes or more? Vera and I have been sitting here in suspense, expecting your scene-painter to start painting some scenery, and it turns out to be just a hoax. Pink pigeons – and that's all! The end!'

At that same round table, before that same ash-tray with its mysterious Arabic characters Bunin one day read me a story he had only just finished writing – the green ink was still all but damp on the paper – a delightful story about the death of an old prince, and when I asked him if it had taken him long to write, Bunin replied, 'About three hours.'

Noticing my astonishment, he added: 'I generally write fast, although I am slow to publish. I wrote the first part of *The Village*, for instance, in about two weeks. Of course I had thought about it for a long time before that, but I put it straight down on paper, in one breath. I made some corrections in copying and in the proofs, but that is as it should be.'

Up to then I had been sure that he wrote very slowly, making a huge number of rough drafts, corrections, versions, polishing every phrase and changing the epithets a dozen times.

I have the impression that such 'flaubertism,' which even today is much in fashion among some writers who apparently believe there is some special skill akin to that of, say, the grinder or the metal-chaser, that can turn the craftsman into an artist, was not in the least characteristic of Bunin, although he himself sometimes spoke of 'polishing,' 'burnishing,' and other nonsense, which in the present age of *mauvisme* can evoke only a smile.

Bunin's power as a descriptive writer lay in his amazingly rapid, almost instantaneous reaction to all outward stimuli and in the ability to find immediately an absolutely accurate verbal expression for them.

He told me that he never used a typewriter, but always wrote in longhand.

'And I advise you not to use one either. After the work is ready in manuscript you can make a typed copy. But the actual work of writing, the creative process lies in the mysterious relationship that arises between head, hand, pen and paper and that is, in fact, the act of creation.'

As he said this Bunin touched his head, then flexed the wrist of the hand in which he held his gold-nibbed fountainpen, touched a sheet of paper with its platinum tip and drew a few flourishes.

'When you type directly, each word you tap out loses all its individuality, whereas when you write it down yourself it becomes, as it were, the material, visible trace of your thought, its pattern. It has not yet lost its secret connection with your soul or, if you prefer, with your organism. So, if that word is false in itself, out of place, tactless, you will not only sense this inwardly, you will also notice it at once with your eyes, by a certain slowing down or speeding up in your pace of writing, or even an actual change in the hand-writing itself. In other words, your handwriting is a unique, inimitable part of your soul and will signal to you if there is something "not quite right!"' he said, somewhat modifying the last line of his poem *The Compass*.

'None shall tempt me from my course, for my soul is guided by some Northern Star, ever with me though I wander far. It shall tell me: this is false.'

I often worked the conversation round to *The Gentleman from San Francisco* because I wanted to hear as much as possible from Bunin about how and why he had written this amazing story, in my opinion opening an entirely new page in the history of Russian literature, which until then – with a few insignificant exceptions – had been famous only for portraying Russian life: national characters, scenery, customs and so on. If any 'foreign bits' happened to occur in our classics, it was only to the extent that they were connected with the fate of Russia or the Russians.

In defiance of all tradition Bunin had written a work in which the only thing Russian was the superb language and that highly perfected plasticity which has always distinguished Russian literature from all world literatures and in which it stands supreme, whereas all the rest in *The Gentleman from San Francisco*, the setting, the characters, the situation, were foreign, or, rather, international – even, if you will, cosmopolitan! – and, above all, ultra-modern, with an American millionaire, a Transatlantic liner, the luxury life in first-class international hotels with their bars and tangos and cars, cocktails, radio, Paris fashions, fabulous wealth and horrifying poverty, everything that flourished particularly on the eve of the First World War and that, at about the same time, Lenin named the highest stage of capitalism – imperialism.

In *The Gentleman from San Francisco* the shadow of the sinking *Titanic* is all the time invisibly present and the final chords of the story contain a grim portent:

'But amidships in the *Atlantis*, the dining halls and ballrooms radiated light and joy, were humming with the voices of the smartly dressed gatherings, were fragrant with the scent of fresh flowers, and the strains of the string orchestra were their song. And again there writhed excruciatingly and at times were quiveringly joined among this throng, among the glitter of lights, silks, diamonds and bared feminine shoulders, the slim and pliant pair of hired lovers – the sinfully demure young woman with lowered eyelashes and an innocent hair-style and the well-built young man with black hair that seemed to be glued in place and a face pale from powder, wearing the most elegant patent-leather shoes and a tight-fitting dress-coat with long tails – a handsome young man, who resembled a huge leech. And no one knew that this pair had long since grown weary of pretending to languish in their blissful torment to the sounds of the shamelessly sad music – nor that far, far below at the bottom of the black hold stood a coffin, consigned to the sombre sultry depths of the ship as it laboured on, overcoming the darkness, the ocean, the blizzard. . . .'

It is sheer delight even to repeat Bunin's words and copy them out in one's own hand!

Before *The Gentleman from San Francisco* Bunin had written a staggeringly powerful anti-colonial story, which was also entirely 'foreign,' *The Brothers*, a story of the tragedy that occurred between a white master and his coloured slave on the fantastically beautiful island of Ceylon. This story might quite easily appear to have been translated from the work of, say, Rudyard Kipling, were it not – once again! – for the marvellous Russian and Bunin's inimitable plastic skill, a skill that gave his descriptions stereoscopic volume and precision, a quality that no world writer of Bunin's time could boast.

'Why are you surprised that I should write such "un-Russian" stories? I never pledged myself to spend my whole life describing Russia and to portray only our Russian life. Every real artist, regardless of his nationality, should possess a free and universal soul that can take in the whole human race; for him there can be no forbidden subject; everything that exists on earth is a subject for art. A universal soul, a universal soul. "Happy am I," ' he said suddenly, lowering his voice to a mysterious murmur, ' "happy am I that your soul, Virgil, is neither mine nor thine." You understand – neither mine nor thine. But universal. In this sense I am, if you will, international. Perhaps even supranational. The main thing is *what* I developed in *The Gentleman from San Francisco* – the symphonic quality inherent in any universal soul. I mean not so much a logical as a musical building-up of prose with changes in rhythm, variations, transitions from one musical key to another – in short, in the kind of counterpoint that Leo Tolstoy made some attempt to apply in *War and Peace*: Bolkonsky's death and so on.'

It may seem curious, perhaps incredible, that at a time when the Civil War had moved down from the north to the south and was raging all around, there should have continued in the house in Knyazheskaya Street, behind the heavy plate-glass windows, a life, more imagined than real, of a quite small circle of people concerned with questions of literature, poetry, criticism, the reading of the Goncourt Brothers in the original, continuing the eternal Moscow arguments about Tolstoy and Dostoevsky and about what exactly the symphonic prose was that had been used for the first time with such fullness in Russian and world literature in *The Gentleman from San Francisco*.

I think it was then that I first became acquainted with some of the ideas of the Goncourt Brothers.

'At the present time in literature it is not enough to create characters that are not at once recognized by the public as old acquaintances, it is not enough to discover an original form of style; you must invent a new lorgnette with which you make people see creatures and things through lenses that have never been used before; you show scenes from an entirely unknown angle, you create a new optics. My brother and I have invented such a lorgnette, and I now see that all young people are using them. . . .'

Perhaps Bunin used these lenses? Anything is possible!

'Banville's reminiscences are very entertaining. Not a word of real truth, his contemporaries look like characters from fairy-tale, but he sees them through a new lens that is all his own: a strange, extremely earthy lens. . . .'

An earthy lens – splendid!

It should not be forgotten that I am writing down in these notes only what memory has retained of those 'literary lessons' that I learned during my acquaintance with Bunin, and he was not at all given to the sedentary, closeted life; on the contrary, he experienced a constant urge to be out among the crowds, to talk to passers-by, to be a witness of street incidents, and certainly not to sit at home giving lessons in craftsmanship to young writers like myself. This can be seen from the very short stories, the literary miniatures he published later, brief sketches from life, such as *The Landau*.

'Everything about death is peculiar to death alone. At the gate of a villa stands a huge old landau and a pair of large black horses: the owner of the villa has come out from town. But there is something unusual, extraordinary about this landau and about these horses. What is it? It turns out that the horses and the landau have been lent to the owner of the villa by his friend, the head of a firm of undertakers. The driver seated on the box actually said:

' "This is a landau from the undertaker's."
'And to crown everything, the driver's black beard is the colour of dry shoe-polish – it has been dyed.'

An earthy lens! Is this not *mauvisme* or, at any rate, its beginnings?

Nearly every day, in any weather Bunin would walk about town. He did not stroll, he walked with a light quick step in a short knee-length overcoat of Moscow cut, with a walking stick and a professorial skull cap instead of a hat – rapid, raptly attentive, gaunt. The character of the Odessa streets constantly changed according to the political situation. At one moment there would suddenly be resurrected the pre-Revolutionary life with the coachmen's trotters covered with blue netting in winter, with flower-sellers and money-changers at the corner of Deribasovskaya and Preobrazhenskaya Streets, opposite the gates of the Wagner House, in the summer, with stock-exchange 'bears' and 'bulls' at the marble-topped tables of the two famous Odessa cafés, the Fanconi and the Robinat, with the night clubs, cabarets, cafés chantants, revue theatres, with the smart English yachts of the Catherine and Black Sea yacht clubs sailing away one after another past the white-stone lighthouse with its brass signal bell out into the open sea, its wide horizon slightly dimmed by the foreign wind, and with silent pictures and a military band conducted by Chernetsky on the Nikolayevsky Boulevard.

Then this would suddenly all be swept away in the course of a single stormy night. In the ominously deserted city only the loud tramp of Red Guard patrols would be heard and the windows of the mansions and banks would rattle with the vibration of the armoured cars as they thundered past with sailors lying on the mudguards, their rifles and Mauser pistols covering the street ahead. And then it would suddenly turn out that the city had been captured by the Petlyura forces or by the bands of some self-styled Ukrainian ataman, and on every street corner peasant lads sporting enormous forelocks, dressed in ragged army greatcoats with their back straps missing, toting their uncleaned rifles butt uppermost, would make people show their passes, and if a person had no pass, let him go on just the same without one. Now British marines would appear in the streets, cheerful fellows trotting along no one knew where with a football at their toes. Now there would be French soldiers strolling down the boulevard in blue greatcoats and gaiters, with double-necked aluminium flasks at their sides filled with red wine and water. Strange carts with two huge wheels would rumble past driven by strapping Negroes, whose eyes always seemed to be bulging with surprise.

I watched Bunin at a soldiers' street market, where he stood amid the crowd with a notebook in his hand, imperturbably and without haste writing down in his clear cuneiform hand the words of a ditty chanted by two brother sailors of the Black Sea Fleet as they did a lively jig, their arms on each other's shoulders, swinging their broad bell-bottoms, while around them stood Chinese pedlars in quilted army jackets, black puttees and round peakless caps, holding coloured paper fans and draped from head to foot with traditional Chinese wares – rattles, little toy birds made out of scraps of worsted wool, expanding paper dragons and tigers on two sticks, lanterns, whistles, lengths of tussore silk, and shoes with thick *papier-mâché* soles.

I remember the nauseating smells of sesame oil, garlic and pungent human sweat that were enough to make one faint.

But Bunin took no notice whatever and calmly continued his work covering page after page with notes.

The most amazing thing was that absolutely no one paid any attention to him, in spite of his professorial appearance, which was quite out of keeping with the street-market crowd. Or perhaps it was just because of his appearance. Who knows what people took him for? It did occur to me that some people might think this gaunt, raw-boned gentleman in his funny skull cap and holding a fountain-pen was one of those fair-ground graphologists, a conjuror, magician or fortune-teller who sold horoscopes, for that would have been quite in the spirit of the time. No one would have been in the least surprised if he had had a parrot or a monkey in a calico shirt perched on his shoulder.

That scene I was to recall much later in the market at Shanghai (the 'Mayor's Temple'), where amid the gilded idols and the fumes of the joss sticks I drew from the sacred urn a folded slip of paper with the following prediction:

'The Phoenix sings before sunrise. The Empress takes no notice, and it is hard to change the fate of the Empress. But your name will endure throughout the ages to come.'

I was surrounded by a prodigiously large and monotonous crowd that seemed to want to crush me and swallow me up. I felt like fainting amid the flowered pink baby jackets, the feverish red satin cushions and eiderdowns, the sandal-wood chests and fresh lithographic portraits of a fat-faced Chinese with puffy eyes, a mandarin in a tunic with a tight upright collar – the great helmsman Mao Tse-tung – while before my eyes floated the rows of poppy-black hieroglyphs of the mysterious prophecy. And I racked my brains trying to guess: who was the phoenix, who was the sun, who was the empress and whose name would endure throughout the ages?

We shall see!

One day some of Bunin's acquaintances, wishing to afford him the opportunity of making a little money, persuaded him to give a reading of his new story *The Dreams of Chang*, which was as yet quite unknown in Odessa. He held out against the idea for a long time, insisting that no one would be interested and no one would come, that the broad public did not know him at all, and that to spend a whole evening reading one story would be simply foolish. Anyone who did come would walk out and the whole undertaking would be a loss to its organizers. In the end, however, he was persuaded, although he warned his friends that he wished to receive the fee for his performance – 'for the disgrace,' as he put it – regardless of what the takings were, even if the hall should be absolutely empty.

'I am not rich enough, gentlemen, to disgrace myself in public – and certainly not for nothing,' Bunin said with dry humour.

Posters were put up in the town, slim programmes were printed, and precisely at the appointed hour in the artists' room of the Odessa College of Music, where concerts for only the most select audiences were held, and also our 'Green Lamp' poetry evenings, which I may one day describe – Bunin appeared. He was pale, exquisitely dressed in an immaculate shirt and a high collar, between the wings of which there was ample room for his pointed beard, which was not quite long enough to cover the broad knot of his silk necktie, in a dark lilac 'peacock-eye' pattern, held in place, I believe, by a pearl tie-pin.

In the cold ill-lighted artists' room sat the organizers. Chief among them was the husband of the stout authoress who looked like Peter the Great, and who had for some time been sitting in the front row of the almost empty hall, just opposite the small table on the platform, where the traditional carafe of boiled water and tumbler stood in bleak array, anxiously adjusting the amethyst brooch on her ample bosom.

With a crackle of starched cuffs Bunin silently shook hands with us all and sat down on a small sofa at the side of the room, placing on it a quite small square briefcase, more like a woman's than a man's, made of excellent English tan leather, which contained the manuscript of his story.

It was perfectly clear that the evening was *already* a failure; there was no attendance.

'Night duty at the undertaker's,' Bunin said after a short silence, glancing up at the dilapidated moulded ceiling. 'I warned you, gentlemen,' he added with a rather bitter smile, in which it was not hard to read a nagging concern about his fate as a writer.

(The hall would be packed, of course, for Igor Severyanin, or Vertinsky! And for Leonid Andreyev, too, not to mention Maxim Gorky. But what can anyone do about it – they are masters of the mind! Who will come to hear me? Only the connoisseurs. . . .)

'Well, gentlemen, shall we begin or shall we all quietly go home?' Bunin asked.

'People seem to be arriving,' the husband of the stout authoress suggested uncertainly. 'Let us wait another quarter of an hour, then make a start.'

'Rather embarrassing,' Bunin muttered. 'I warned you no one would come to hear me.'

'How can you say such things, Ivan Alexeyevich! They'll come to hear you if they'll come to hear anybody!' one of the organizers called out in a false voice. "It's all because the notices were put up late and there weren't enough announcements in the paper, but the real trouble is that a Haidamak uprising is expected tonight. Surely you can see for yourself—'

'You need not try to console me,' Bunin said firmly and held up one of the notices to look at it. There, in the very title of the story was an idiotic and typically provincial misprint – 'The Dreams of Clang' – that made it quite meaningless.

Bunin's face twisted, as though from a sudden blow in the solar plexus. He even gasped, but at once took a grip on himself and waved the matter aside.

'Oh, who cares!'

Perhaps it was because beyond the tall windows and cream waves of curtains a volley of shots occasionally rang out in the street, striking the window panes like hard rubber balls and evoking pictures of the dark tense city with its locked and barricaded gates and armoured cars stationed at street corners – someone muttered something about Blok's poem

The Twelve, which had only recently got through to us across the demarcation line and had at once aroused elation among the young people.

'Rat-tat-tat! And from the houses only echo bounces back. . . .'

'I can't understand what people see in this *Twelve* thing, or how a poet could sink so low as to make up these vulgar uncouth street ditties,' Bunin said abruptly, with a shrug of his shoulders. ' "Vanka and Katka out on the booze. She got Kerensky notes in her shoes. . . ." Russian literature has never reached such degradation before. And this man was a poet, always a mannered one, of course, but a poet for all that. There was a time when he wrote poems about the Madonna, the Beautiful Lady "radiant among the ikon lamps. . . ." And now what? What is this Jesus Christ in a white halo of roses? Perhaps he meant to say wreath? Not even an elementary feeling for the Russian language. Typical modernism!'

As he said this Bunin looked me straight in the face with eyes that were filled – not with anger but with a real hatred. His cheeks had suddenly become hollow and even bonier than before.

'You, of course, are enchanted with it? Naturally! You probably consider *The Scythians* a great prophetic work. . . . Of course – "we, the shield between two hostile races – the Mongols and Europe." And what are these machines of steel where the integral breathes? How can an integral breathe, I ask you? And not just anywhere, but in machines of steel! Ravings! Decadent rubbish!'

I was reduced to confusion, because for some time and without telling Bunin, I had been in love with Blok, and whereas the first book I had asked for had been Bunin's poems, the second, which I had bought myself, with my own money, had been Alexander Blok's *Snowy Night*.

I cannot say that I liked *The Twelve* in those days. In many ways the poem repelled me, as one always is repelled, incidentally, in literature by a new and completely untried form without which new content is impossible, particularly if this content is revolution.

I was not then quite equal to the revolution.

But even then *The Twelve* astonished me with its word-painting – authentic, accurate, substantial, not realist but materialist, quite unlike anything else.

Black evening. White snow. Powdered on top, ice below. A woman falling – down she goes. Lights, lights, lights. Rifles tight over shoulders slung. Electric torch from shaft-bow hung. A windtorn poster – what's it say? 'All Power to the Constituent Assembly!' You've been guzzling Mignon chocolate! Can't see each other four paces away. . . .

Those four paces! Not two, not three, but four! How those four fateful paces wounded the imagination of many a poet! How hard it was to get rid of them.

Not to speak of the brilliant lines: '. . . *nézhnoi póstupyu nadvyúzhnoi, snézhnoi róssypyu zhemchúzhnoi,*' perhaps the best lines in world poetry.

As for *The Scythians*, I accepted the whole poem, not only with admiration but with a sense of genuine awe on reading these prophetic ponderous iambics, which have retained their power over my soul and over my imagination to this day.

It all fitted with the conception I had in those days of Russia's destiny; everything found a response in me.

'. . . and visions marvellously caught . . . the luminous Gallic wit, the German dusk's new worlds of thought.'[1]

Particularly, those visions marvellously caught.

I was not in the least frightened by 'Your gloss-faced Europe. . . we'll lure. . . and turn on you again, swooping, our Asiatic faces.' Nor was I put off by the barbarian lute or any of the other sharp edges of that remarkable Eurasian poem, which revealed to me a whole new world of the awakening East.

[1] I am indebted to Mr Jack Lindsay for these lines from his translation of *The Scythians.*—R.D.

I was a soldier, a real soldier who had been at the front line, and I was not easily frightened, certainly not by the revolution. The soldiers loved the revolution. It was for them the longed-for relief from war. This was my advantage over Bunin, who feared and hated the soldiers and sailors who were making the October Revolution, the greatest revolution history had ever known; they all seemed to him to be the same: stolid, cruel, brutalized by bloodshed, unbridled, not revolutionaries but rebels, destroyers of Russia.

I, who had lived with them at war for almost two years, who had hunted and fed the lice with them, eaten with them, and taught some of them to read and even sat in a water-logged dug-out near Smorgon reading Gogol and Tolstoy to to them in the lulls between fighting – incidentally, they liked *Anna Karenina* very much – who had lain with them, wounded or gassed on the rotten straw of field hospitals, who knew all their cherished peasant (and quite legitimate) dreams of land, freedom, and universal peace, of overthrowing the hated House of Romanov, destroying the landowners, kulaks and capitalists, of the approaching Revolution, and who fully sympathized with these dreams, although they had no direct connection with my own personal life – or so it seemed to me at the time! – I was not at all afraid of these people, who were not in the least cruel or bloodthirsty, but simple, kind, decent, fair-minded Russian peasants and workers, tormented and driven to the limit of their endurance by a criminal war and centuries of injustice.

This was the real Russia, not the one conjured up by Bunin, who had given way to shameful terror of the revolution, a terror that was characteristic of so many Russian intellectuals in those days.

I remembered the autobiographical notes which Bunin wrote two years before the revolution: 'In the early stages I heard all kinds of things besides praise of my artistic gifts. Some people even stooped so low as to suggest that I was simply frightened by the revolution, as a landowner (although I had never owned land in my life). . . .'

Alas, it is painful to admit, but I see now quite clearly that Bunin *was* afraid of the revolution. I think it was this fear of the revolution that was the main tragedy of the Bunin I observed in the years of which I write.

'You, of course, do not agree with me about *The Scythians* and *The Twelve?*' he said sharply. 'I am afraid you, and many young people of your age and position, your friends, have taken a wrong and slippery path that will lead you to destruction. . . .' He gave me another piercing glance and laughed drily. 'However, gentlemen, if we are to begin it's time we began.' And with these words he walked through the side-door, up the steps on to the stage, bowed curtly to a light ripple of applause, sat down at the rickety table, drew out of his briefcase a magazine off-print of *The Dreams of Chang*, glanced at his watch and without another look at the half-empty, poorly lighted hall, read in a clear, resonant voice with excellent diction the whole of his splendid (also symphonic) story, beginning with those wonderful phrases that ring out like a solemn music:

'What does it matter of whom we speak? Any that have lived or live upon earth deserve this much. One day Chang perceived the world and the captain, his master, with whom his earthly existence is joined. And since that day a whole six years have passed, trickled away, like sand in a ship's hour-glass. Again it is night – dream or reality? – and once more morning has come – reality or dream?'

Surely it mattered little to all these people caught in the midst of a revolution, in a besieged city, sitting in a cold, half-empty, badly lighted hall, what happened to a dissipated drunkard captain and his dog Chang, purchased 'on a cold and dusty day on a broad Chinese river' and brought on the ship to Odessa?

Nevertheless, they sat without stirring through the whole forty-five minutes of the reading, bewitched by the music of this scenic symphonic prose with its changes of rhythm,

83

syncopation and phrasing, like sombre chords played by a great organist.

'. . . and on a sudden the church doors are flung open and into Chang's eyes and heart there floods a wonderful scene, all vibrant with sound and song. Before him is a dim Gothic palace, the lights gleaming like scarlet stars, a whole forest of tropical plants, an oaken coffin set high on a black platform, a black crowd of people, two women of statuesque beauty and dressed in deep mourning – like two sisters of different ages – and above it all – the roar, the thunder, the choir of angels lifting their voices in a wail of sorrowful joy, the exultation, the tumult, the magnificence – a celestial song that transcends everything. And every hair in Chang's coat stands on end with the pain and ecstasy of this sonorous vision. . . .'

A sonorous vision. . . .

Only for one second did the listeners' attention waver from *The Dreams of Chang*, when beyond the windows, in the dark abyss of the besieged city a short burst of machine-gun fire was heard, followed by the boom of a hand grenade, and a voice said softly in the middle of the hall: 'Gentlemen, I think they're shooting in Malaya Arnautskaya Street. . . .'

That night I saw Bunin home through the dark, ominously quiet city. He seemed to be hostilely silent and, wishing to divert him from depressing thoughts, I kept trying to say something that would please him.

'Ivan Alexeyevich, a great deal of your work must have been translated into other languages, I suppose?'

'Good heavens, man!' he replied irritably. 'Judge for yourself. One of my stories, for instance, begins like this: "Na Fóminoi nedélye, v yásnyi chut rózovi vécher, v tu preléstnuyu póru, kogdá. . . ."[1] Just try to say that in English or French, try to preserve the music of the Russian language,

[1] In St Thomas' week, on a clear, pink-tinged evening, at that delightful hour when. . . .

the subtlety of the scene-painting. . . . "V *tu preléstnuyu póru, kogdá.* . . ." Impossible, Aud what am I worth without that? No, I am very little known abroad – or here, in Russia either, for that matter,' he added bitterly.

One day Bunin told me that if he were very rich he would never live in one place, building up a home, a flat, a library, a wardrobe. He would rather travel all over the world, staying at good, comfortable hotels and living there as long as he wished and, as soon as he grew tired of the place, moving on somewhere else, taking only the minimum of luggage – one or two suitcases with bare necessities. Nothing superfluous. Never send a dirty shirt to the laundry, just throw it away because it would be more interesting and much easier to buy a new one. The same with suits and shoes. The suitcase would contain only notebooks, paper and the various odds and ends he had grown used to.

'Like your ash-tray?'

'Exactly.'

He spoke in a joking way, but I believe there was a great deal of truth in what he said.

I had the impression that the Bunins always seemed to be camping out among other people's furniture, pictures, curtains, crockery and lamps. Their only possessions were their clothes, their bedding, and a pair of slim English leather suitcases plastered with foreign hotel labels.

Oh, yes, and about labels.

One day I asked him what literary trend he considered himself as adhering to.

'Oh, what a lot of nonsense all these trends are! According to the critics I am a decadent, a symbolist, a mystic, a realist, a neorealist, a god-seeker, a naturalist and God knows what else. They have stuck so many labels on me that I feel like a suitcase that has travelled all round the world – plastered all over with a lot of gawdy labels. But can any of this explain what kind of artist I really am? Not one bit! I am myself, unique and inimitable, like everyone else on earth, and that is the heart of the matter.' He gave me one of his sidelong 'Chekhovian' glances. 'And you, sir, may expect the same fate. You will be plastered all over with labels, like a travelling bag. Mark my words !'

He had plenty of opportunities to leave Odessa, where he was in some danger, and go abroad, particularly since, as I have said, he travelled light and liked roaming from town to town, and country to country. But in Odessa he was stuck: he did not want to become an emigré, cut off from his country; he was stubbornly hoping for a miracle – for the Bolsheviks to be defeated, Soviet rule overthrown and his return to Moscow amid the triumphant ringing of the Kremlin bells. But what kind of Moscow? I doubt whether he had any clear idea. To the old Moscow he had been accustomed to? This may have been the reason why he stayed in Odessa in the spring of 1919, when it was occupied by the Red Army and Soviet rule was established for a few months.

By this time Bunin was so deeply compromised by his counter-revolutionary views, which incidentally he made no attempt to hide, that he could have been shot without further ado, and probably would have been shot but for his old Odessa friend Nilus, the artist, who lived in the same house as the Bunins, in the attic, the very attic that was described in *The Dreams of Chang*. It was no ordinary attic, but a warm attic 'redolent of cigars, with carpets, old furniture, pictures, and brocade. . . .'

Well, as I was saying, if Nilus had not displayed frantic energy – he telegraphed Lunacharsky in Moscow and almost went down on his knees to the chairman of the Odessa Revolutionary Committee – anything might have happened.

At all events Nilus obtained a special so-called 'safe-conduct' for the life and property of Academician Bunin, which was pinned to the rich varnished door of the house in Knyazheskaya Street.

. . . A detachment of armed sailors and soldiers of the Special Department marched up to the front door of the house. Vera Nikolayevna, who was looking out of the window, saw the blue collars and orange unbuttoned sheepskins flapping open, and slid limply to the floor. Bunin, however, stomped noisily over the parquet floors to the door, planted himself firmly on the threshold, throwing back his clenched fists in a grotesque gesture, while great tremors crossed his blanched face with its trembling beard and terrible eyes.

'If anyone so much as dares to cross my doorstep. . . .' He did not shout the words but somehow ground them out, working his jaw and baring his strong sharp yellowish teeth, 'I'll gnaw the first man's throat, and then you can kill me! I want no more of this life!'

And at once I remembered the lines he had written earlier: '. . . then lead me out and stab me at a stroke – if not, beware! My teeth shall tear you all and from none be torn!'

I was paralysed with horror.

But all ended well. The Special Department men read the safe-conduct with its Soviet stamp and signature, looked very surprised, and someone even swore mildly at the Revolutionary Committee, but they did not want to go against the decision of a power they considered sacred, and marched away silently down the hushed deserted street, past the white acacia trees, whose rough black-grey bark was still dry from winter but already showed a hint of tender bast in the deep cracks.

I watched the whole scene through the window, so that between me and the Special Detachment men hung a large outdoor thermometer with a mercury ball, which reflected some still rather misty gleams of an already hot spring sunshine.

And suddenly I again saw and at once recognized her, the girl from the Kovalevsky villa, whom I had described on Bunin's advice five years before.

Now she was about seventeen. She stood among the sailors and soldiers reading the safe-conduct, her army sheepskin flapping open, with a white Siberian fur cap pushed off her perspiring olive-brown forehead. In her small firm hand she held a dragoon's rifle, her teeth were clenched, her chin jutted out like a little shoe, and from her dark face came the moonlight glow of a pair of narrow angry and yet magically alluring eyes.

Our glances met and she threatened me – a young man, her enemy, in the flat of the counter-revolutionary Bunin – with her short handy rifle.

And once more we lost sight of each other, though not for long, and life that had for a moment seemed like a page of Victor Hugo resumed its usual course.

Surprisingly, when I met her again quite soon I did not at once recognize her.

'The working, organizational period began,' I wrote hot on the heels of events in my Notes on the Civil War.

'The new Bolshevik government allowed everyone who had remained in the city the right to assemble and discuss collectively on what lines their life should be organized. In a large and, as it seemed to me at the time, elegantly decorated hall of the so-called "Literaturka," where not so long ago servants in frock coats had been attending to the needs of aesthetes in velvet jackets and actresses with painted eyelashes, there now stood rough chairs and benches brought up from the janitor's room, and on these sat a lot of upset, uprooted people, most of them refugees from the north. They now had to define their attitude to Soviet rule, which had at last caught up with them on the shores of the Black Sea.

'Bunin sat in the corner, his chin resting on the handle of a thick stick. He was jaundiced, angry and deeply lined. His thin neck protruded tautly from the collar of his starched shirt. His puffy eyes were fierce and penetrating. His whole body seemed to twitch and he craned his neck as though his collar was too tight for him. He was the most irreconcilable.

Several times he leapt to his feet and banged his stick angrily on the floor.'

Yuri Olesha described the scene in much the same way later.

'When at the meeting of artists, writers and poets he banged the floor with his stick at us, young people, and looked like an angry old man, he was actually only forty-two. But by then he was already really an old man! And what was more, he was a fierce, gnarled old man – a real greybeard.'

Though Olesha was wrong about Bunin's age (he was then nearly fifty), it was not so much a matter of age, as the impression of age. That impression corresponds with mine. Bunin *was* an angry old man.

The young people he hammered on the floor against were Bagritsky, Olesha and I. . . .

We used to be referred to in the town in those days with a mixture of fear and surprise as 'those three!'

I continued to visit Bunin, although it was clear that our paths were moving further and further apart. I was still passionately fond of him, and I don't want to add: 'as an artist.' I loved him completely, as a person, an individual as well. There seemed to be no perceptible cooling in his attitude to me, although I did notice that he would more and more often scan me closely, as though trying to comprehend something that puzzled him in the soul of a young man of the period infected by the Revolution, to read his deepest thoughts.

He even became rather pernickety at times. One day, for instance, he noticed that I was wearing a gold chain as a bracelet with a kind of pendant on it.

He frowned.

'What foppishness is this? You are not a girl, to be wearing a gold bracelet.'

'It's not gold,' I said. 'It's gilded copper and hollow.'

'That's even worse. Real gold might not be so bad. But a hollow fake won't do at all. Remember this: a man should use and adorn himself with – if he has decided to adorn himself at all – only with what is real. . . . No imitation, no fakes! What is that dangling from it?'

'It's the shell splinter they took out of the upper part of my thigh,' I said rather boastfully, but blushing to the roots of my hair.

Bunin took my hand and guided on to his palm the sharp fragment of copper with a three-figure number stamped on it, part of the driving band of a German shell, which would certainly have ended my life had it struck me in the head. Bunin examined the fragment from all angles.

'Was this in your body?'

'Yes, in the upper part of the thigh,' I repeated with satisfaction.

'Then why don't you wear it on a plain steel chain. That would be much better. Hollow American gold is not worthy of your real,' he stressed the word, 'shell splinter. It only degrades it. How did it happen? But don't make anything up.'

'I was thrown into the air and, when I opened my eyes, I was looking at the earth under one cheek and there were chunks of earth falling on me and a lot of dust flying about and the explosion had been so close it smelt as if someone had been burning a celluloid comb near by.'

'Well, wear it and good luck to you, if you want to appear richer than you really are,' Bunin said after a little thought.

It was a sultry summer. The city was deserted and dead, the stalls closed, the market silent, except for a few peasants hurriedly bartering flour for town articles. Tobacco and matches were entirely absent.

I brought Bunin a large magnifying glass which I had taken out of the yellow deal box of our Afon Panorama. This panorama, which we had purchased during our trip abroad, was considered a very precious article in our house and held third place after mother's piano and the chiming wall clock in the dining room, which we had won in a raffle.

The round magnifying glass in the top of the box, to which was attached a brass hook, had the magic effect of bringing nearer the enlarged and brightly coloured postcards of the famous Aya Sofia mosque with its spear-like minarets at the corners, or the old cemetery in Scutari with the white marble posts of the moslem tombs and the almost black cyprus trees against a background of a chocolate-box ultramarine sky without a single cloud.

I wrapped up the glass in a sheet of the best paper I possessed, on which I had written the following madrigal:

'To Ivan Bunin, on presenting him with a magnifying glass.

'Oh, mentor, take this magic glass. Its warmth shall to your refuge pass, Fate and matchlessness despite, your fragrant weed with sun to light.

'Revolution's equal rights and troubled days leave none but heathen gods in heaven to reign. Now even Phoebe all his debts repays. Once you served him; now he serves you again.'

Ignoring my attempt at stylization, Bunin rolled a cigarette with the remains of some third-rate black tobacco, took the magnifying glass and caught the tip of his cigarette in a bunch of sunrays filtering through the dusty windowpane from the now utterly silent city.

A wisp of smoke appeared from the pinpoint of light, like a rick catching fire somewhere far away in the steppe, and Bunin began to smoke, using the familiar ash-tray which I knew so well and which now seemed less well polished than in former days.

'Thank you,' he said, pressing my hand. 'You've done me a great service. I am indebted to you.'

In autumn the town changed hands again. This time it

was occupied by Denikin. And on one of the city's dark wet mornings – a real Paris morning! – I read Bunin my latest, carefully corrected and recopied story about a young man. This time out of sheer obstinacy I had made him a student, who rather like Pushkin's Herman was a gambler and wanted at all costs to win a lot of money at cards, while another young man – for the same reasons of obstinacy and contradiction I made him an actor in a small revue theatre – was jealous of the student and even wanted to shoot him with a revolver but quite accidentally failed to do so. All this, of course, was enacted with the help of a bewitchingly beautiful ballet dancer against a background of a doomed bourgeois city besieged by the Red Army. I realize now that the value of the story lay in its attempt to convey the sense of social doom on the eve of a revolutionary uprising, when in the working-class districts on the outskirts the underground was bringing out its hidden weapons and 'the new day rising in a band of light beyond the black factory chimneys was the last day of Babylon.'

Bunin listened in silence, his elbow resting on the polished table, and I watched his face fearfully for signs of irritation or perhaps even anger. But his eyes were puckered wearily at the corners and staring into the distance, as though he could indeed see above those Verhaeren-like black factory chimneys the bloody revolutionary dawn, and his whole figure, even the limp fingers in which he held the smoking cigarette over the copper bowl of the ash-tray, expressed a deep disappointment, almost pain.

'I was trying to apply your principle of symphonic prose,' I said, when I had finished reading.

He looked at me and said bitterly, as though replying to his own thoughts: 'Well, I suppose it was to be expected. I no longer see myself here. You are moving away from me towards Leonid Andreyev. But tell me this. Could you, like your hero, kill a person in order to take possession of his wallet?'

'I couldn't, but my character—'

'Untrue!' Bunin said sharply, almost shouted. 'Don't blame everything on your character! Every character is the author himself.'

'But surely! Raskolnikov—'

'Aha! I knew you would mention that name. A starving young man with an axe under his jacket. Who knows what Dostoevsky went through while he was inventing this Raskolnikov of his. The name alone! I believe,' Bunin went on, dropping his voice, 'that in those moments Dostoevsky was himself Raskolnikov. I hate your Dostoevsky,' he suddenly exclaimed again, passionately. 'An utterly revolting writer with all his heaping of one thing on top of another, the ghastly carelessness of his completely affected, unnatural language that no one ever spoke or speaks, with all those importunate, wearisome repetitions, prolixities and sheer inarticulacy. . . . He keeps grabbing you by the ears and pushing your nose into this impossible mess he has invented, into a kind of mental vomit. And besides, it's so mannered, so artificial, so unnatural. The legend of the Grand Inquisitor!' Bunin cried with a grimace of disgust, and burst out laughing. 'That's where all that has happened to Russia now springs from, all the decadence, the modernism, the revolution, young people like yourself, infected to the bone with Dostoevskyism – no aim in life, lost, spiritually and physically crippled by the war, not knowing what to do with their energy, abilities, their quite considerable, even enormous talents. . . . But what's the use of talking about it!' he concluded with a gesture of despair.

Perhaps he was the first person in the world to speak of the lost generation.

But our Russian – my – generation was not lost. It did not perish, although it might well have perished. The war had crippled it, but the Great Revolution saved it and healed it. Whatever I am and have been, I owe my life and my work to the Revolution. And to it alone.

I am a son of the Revolution. A bad son, perhaps. But nevertheless, a son.

This was in the last few months before we parted forever. Here are some of Bunin's thoughts of those days that struck me by their *unconventionality*.

'For all his genius, you know, Leo Tolstoy is by no means irreproachable as an artist. There is a great deal of raw, super-fluous stuff in his work. One day I should like to take, for instance, *Anna Karenina* and rewrite it. Not write it in my own way, but – how shall I put it? – make a clean copy, removing all the prolixities, leaving out one or two things, making some of the sentences more exact, better propor-tioned, but, of course, not adding a word of my own, leaving everything of Tolstoy's absolutely intact. I may do that one day. As an experiment, of course, only for myself, not for print. Although I am deeply convinced that Tolstoy, edited like that – not by some Strakhov but by a real artist – would be read with even more pleasure and would acquire those readers who cannot cope with his novels simply because of their stylistic imperfections.'

One can imagine what a storm of the most contradictory feelings were awakened in my feeble young soul by such thoughts, which my mentor expressed in a very simple, even matter-of-fact tone without any affectation or desire to *épater*, as people liked to say in those days, but with that irresistible force of inward conviction that works more power-fully than truth itself.

To speak like this of Dostoevsky and Tolstoy! It drove me mad. But – why not? Even then I suspected that the artist's most valuable quality was complete, absolute fearless in-dependence of opinion. After all, even the great Leo Tolstoy himself, quite calmly and without regard for anything or anyone, had subjected Shakespeare himself to annihilating criticism, not only casting doubt on the value of his ideas but simply ridiculing him as an extremely mediocre, or rather, perfectly useless scribbler. And what had Tolstoy done with

Wagner, with the contemporary French poets, with the great Baudelaire and Verlaine! . . . The mind boggled. Towards the end of his life it even looked as if he were going to set about Pushkin. He had certainly come near to doing so!

And what of it?

Tolstoy remained Tolstoy: Shakespeare, Shakespeare; Wagner, Wagner; and Baudelaire, Baudelaire, Everything remained as it was. Even a giant like Tolstoy had been unable to change the world's tune.

But this I realized only much later, when I had matured in mind and heart. In those days I listened to my mentor with a thrill of horror.

In answer to my question about Scriabin, about his advanced music, his attempt to find some connection between sound and light, his strange orchestration and unprecedented counterpoint, Bunin responded approximately as follows:

'Scriabin? Humph! You want to know what Scriabin is and what his music amounts to, for example, his tone-poem L'Extase? Well, I can tell you. Imagine the Large Hall of the Moscow Conservatoire. The gleam of the chandeliers. The oval portraits of the great composers, the huge organ with the symphony orchestra before it – violins, music desks, the dazzling boiled shirt-fronts and white ties of the musicians, each a celebrity in his own field. The most select audience imaginable: the great Moscow connoisseurs and music critics, the girl students, professors, actors, the richest of the rich, famous beauties, officers, the cream of the Moscow intelligentsia. The suspense is slightly feverish. The whole hall is electrified. Impatience rises to breaking point, but at last the conductor sweeps back his coat-tails, flourishes his baton and the famous symphony begins – the last revolutionary word in contemporary modernistic decadent music. Now then – how shall I explain this symphony in the most popular manner? I shall try. Off go the violins! All at sixes and sevens. But so far it is still more or less generally accepted

95

and in keeping with the traditions of the famous Moscow Conservatoire. Then all of a sudden a violin begins to squeal desperately, like a stuck pig: Ee-e-eeh! Ee-e-eeh!' And Bunin made a terrible face and without a trace of embarrassment screamed so that he could be heard from one end of the flat to the other. 'And then comes a sickening, soul-rending howl from a trumpet—'

'Ioann, you must be quite mad!' Vera Nikolayevna exclaimed in horror, running into the room and pushing her fingers into her ears.

'I am giving a popular explanation of Scriabin's tone-poem *L'Extase*,' Bunin said drily, sending me a piercing glance. 'You, of course, are enchanted with the "new music," as befits a modern poet and admirer of Dostoevsky and Leonid Andreyev?'

'I have never heard any of Scriabin's symphonic work, but I very much like his piano pieces,' I said, wishing to maintain independence. (I actually intended writing a story in which the hero played one of Scriabin's preludes. . . .)

But after one glance at Bunin and the venomous expression on his haemorrhoidal face, I added hesitantly, 'But my hero could play Grieg, of course.'

'Perhaps Tchaikovsky?' Bunin asked in a strange tone.

'Yes, of course, perhaps Tchaikovsky,' I said.

'There you are,' Bunin replied, now sounding quite casual and cheerful. 'Grieg or Tchaikovsky, a sad Levitan landscape, Chekhov's gentle humour. . . . The heroine, of course, is a former actress. Yellow leaves. Solitude. Water colours—' And quite suddenly: 'Do you like Andersen?'

'Well, er – yes.'

'Just as I thought. Vera, he actually likes Andersen. Now the fashion is for Andersen. Or even for Alexander Green. Very well, when you write your story, you must make sure that besides Grieg, Tchaikovsky, Levitan and Chekhov, you don't forget Andersen; mention the poor toy soldier, the charred paper rose, or something of the kind and, if you can manage it, link it up with one of Green's pipe-smoking captains and a pint of peach brandy – and your success with the middle-aged intellectual ladies of the provinces will be assured. Oh no, you needn't smile, my dear sir. It is these ladies, the admirers of Green and Grieg, who make a writer's reputation as a romantic, almost a classic. Believe me, a much-baited literary wolf. You will have cause to remember me more than once.' And then with no apparent connection he added suddenly, 'But does it really matter? What matters is learning to write simply.'

'Do you not write simply?' I exclaimed.

'No, not in that sense. What I mean is to write with absolute simplicity. So that nothing could be more simple. Noun, verb, full-stop – with perhaps an occasional subordinate clause when absolutely necessary, but always childishly simple. Like a fable. A prayer. A fairy-tale. The noise was heard by a nightingale. The crow saw the cheese. The crow liked the cheese. Or perhaps something like *The Tale of the Goat.*'

And his voice was mysteriously ominous as he began softly : 'Are they wolf's eyes or stars amid the tree trunks on the edge of the wood? Midnight, late autumn, frost. The bare oak above me is all ashimmer in the light of the stars, dry silver crunches under foot. The paths trodden in summer have hardened to stone. You are alone, alone, little Goat of this terrible autumn tale! And in the sleeping frost those hungry wolf-like, God-like eyes burst into flower.'

There was, of course, simplicity in this, but not at all the simplicity of which Bunin had spoken. It was not a fable not a prayer, not a fairy-tale, but rather a parable. Or even more probably a vision. Of the Goat and the Wolf. Both with a capital letter. A fearful prophetic vision – a parable written in silver on the blue-black, almost winter sky : a bare oak shimmering in the starlight, and under it, all alone, completely and terribly alone on this frosty midnight, a goat, an old goat with gaunt bony flanks, a beggarly Russian goat with the wise, haggard, tormented face of Ivan

Bunin, with those tear-drained eyes of a martyr and of a great sinner who could not tear his gaze from the avenging eyes of God, blazing, bursting into flower in a steely frost like the eyes of some ancient glittering frost-coated were-wolf, and this lean, sinewy wolf with its gnashing yellow teeth was at the same time a new incarnation of that same Bunin – simultaneously a Goat with the eyes of a Buddha, and a Wolf, a victim and a slim-bearded executioner in a long cavalry greatcoat reaching to the ground, a devil and a god.

The worst of it was that I was gradually losing control of my dwindling consciousness and sinking into an oppressive phantasmal world of indescribable dreams, aware only of the leaden throbbing of my blood, heated to a temperature of 40 degrees Celsius, and at one moment I was the Goat and another the Wolf, stalking one another along the paths frozen hard as stone.

I shivered and froze in the Arctic cold, my teeth chattered, a mortal nausea rose in my throat, and there was not a drop of warmth anywhere, as though I was in a deserted armoured train of steel, amid endless expanses, amid these thin, cold hospital blankets of the eternally frozen Arctic Ocean, over which the short thick curtain of the Aurora Borealis cast its sequin gleams, making the cold all the more intense, while straight into my eyes, from just above my head, shone the electric bulb of the North Star, that kept glaring, glaring murderously at me with its feeble filaments that could never glare enough.

I was visited by prophetic dreams, which I immediately forgot, but one of them did leave a faint trace in my memory.

. . . gasping for breath, a man was running across the burning stone courtyards of the Monastery of Choizhin-lama, one of the cruellest and most terrible of all lamas, who bore the title of State Oracle. At one time Choizhin-lama had

98

requested the Emperor of Manchuria to name his monastery and had received the title 'Bestower of Bliss,' which was now inscribed on a shield at the entrance to the main temple in the Manchurian, Mongolian, Chinese and Tibetan languages.

The man was being pursued. He ran into the temple, which was covered outside and inside with pictures of severed human heads and entails hanging on varicoloured silk threads. These pictures symbolized the enemies of religion and were there to show what would be the fate of unbelievers and heretics in the after life.

This man was a Revolutionary and was running away from the City temporarily captured by the Insurgent Lamas. He hoped to escape in the temple by hiding behind one of the seats in the left-hand row, which was occupied during services by one of the highest lamas, the halibo-lama, before whom were laid out the instruments of worship, the bells, tambourines, cymbals, drums, seashells and the steel prayer stick ochir which gave the priest the power of life and death. All around there were pictures of heaven and also of a blazing and freezing hell with the naked figures of the tormented sinners. Three huge coral masks portraying the terrible God Zhamsaran with gaping jaws stared down on the man with hollow eye-sockets, and since the man had knocked a bronze gong with his shoulder as he ran into the cluttered temple, the air was vibrating with a muffled boom that set the bluish wisps of smoke from the slim long candles quivering and scattered grey ash on the silver trays.

Then came the tramping of feet in Mongolian boots and the Enemies ran into the temple and seized the man, who was clutching with both hands at a small gilded figure of a woman, a Buddha with an alluringly slim waist, a fleeting smile on her thin, goat-like lips, guilefully lowered lashes and shapely legs, crossed so that their narrow gilded soles were somehow turned up to heaven.

The man flung himself on the floor, but was seized, dragged along and pinioned against a blue pillar with gilded patterns. And then a shaven-headed Lama, gnashing his teeth, drew from his belt a Chinese shepherd's knife in a sandal-wood sheath embossed with soft silver, and drove the narrow, deep-groved blade into the chest of the Revolutionary, and thrust his muscular wrestler's arm bared to the shoulder, into the purple-red, seemingly incandescent wound-flower and tore out the heart, and then kicked the prostrate body aside like carrion.

And this body of the Man was I, and it was my heart that they tied with a silken thread to the banner of the counter-revolutionary uprising, and it flew above the galloping horsemen and the flowing manes of the horses as they scattered the tops of the yellow poppies with their hooves, above the jagged peaks of the Hingan Range, above the Gobi Desert over which rustled the sultry silk of the Chinese wind.

. . . I lay in the middle of the scorching monastery yard with my heart torn out, under the gaze of small bronze lions that looked like little frogs coated with green snail-shells of wool; the choking fumes of dried herbs floated up from the censers, and Bogdo Gegen's yellow carriage flashed between the red gilded pillars of the monastery gates, from whose heavy yet graceful pantiled roof with upturned corners there hung silent bells. And at that very moment I was suddenly transformed into that iron, rough-cast, bow-legged man with his stumps of arms agonizedly twisted upwards and a jagged hole through his rectangular body which I was later to see – forty years ahead – among the rubble heaps of Rotterdam, which the fascists had blown to pieces, and the seagulls of the gloomy North Sea were flying with desperate wailing cries to and fro through the gap in my chest where my heart had used to beat. . . .

Oh, if only people knew what torture it is to be an iron man-city with one's heart torn out, doomed to eternal immobility and silence on one's concrete pedestal, and at the same time to be stretched out on an ice-flow with dead, staring eyes that reflect the light of the tiny North star.

And when I could bear this torture no longer and was ready to plunge forever into the icy water, into those fathomless depths, where the cigar-shaped *Nautilus* was feeling its way along an ice corridor in the magical green water and Captain Nemo, with arms folded on his chest, was gasping in the last drops of oxygen, I began to have divine visions, which were of such celestial beauty that poor earthly Time stopped altogether, and there began some other, higher Time that made my body imperishable.

I experienced a great uplifting of the spirit. It was *L'Extase*, with that high-pitched wail of the trumpet ascending above the muffled whisper of the violins and reaching its highest imaginable point, the very zenith of bliss, and remaining poised there forever.

Sometimes I seemed to float to the surface and began to feel, though still very faintly, my drained, exhausted body under its thin hospital blanket that admitted the Arctic cold.

Sensation partially returned and I became aware of the persistent smell of chloroform and carbolic, which made the strange void in which I was suspended seem like an enormous deserted railway terminal, the typhus-stricken Zhmerinka of my wartime nightmares, filled with concrete rumblings and a chaos of luggage, from which there suddenly popped up beside me the familiar figures of my father in an autumn overcoat, funny-coloured old women's mittens and my younger brother Zhenya – the future Evgeni Petrov – in a moth-eaten camel-hair cap with its long earflaps wound round his neck like a scarf. They were standing before me, their arms dangling limp with despair, and I saw the tears running down their cheeks and father's greying beard, and Zhenya's dark eyes brimming with pain, pity and horror.

I realized they thought that I was dying, that at any

moment, before their very eyes I might breathe my last, or
that I had perhaps already died and my body was stiffening,
and at the same time in every fibre of my awakening, exult-
ing soul I already knew for sure that the crisis had passed,
and that I should now live, and live very long, perhaps
forever, and though I was aware of this surging tide of life
within me I could tell them nothing, not even smile. . . .

I heard their faint voices repeating my name from afar,
but from an even greater distance I could still hear the sounds
of battle, which gave me some intimation of what was
going on in the city, of the last hours of its Siege, and of the
evacuation that appeared to me as a bare forest of blasts from
ships' sirens.

It may have been at that very hour that my Bunin was
leaving his country forever!

And once again I plunged into an abyss of happy dreams,
and when I eventually awoke I realized from various signs
that a quite new life had begun around me, and young
poets were writing on anything they could lay hands on; on
the other side of Mendeleyev's table of elements, for instance,
which for convenience they cut up into rectangular strips;
on sheets of a very thin pale-pink paper of the old world –
then known as 'chemists' paper,' astonishingly flimsy, in-
capable of surviving the epoch, almost weightless, disinte-
grating at a touch like ash; or on stout reliable pages torn out
of the prison register in which, under the old regime, sums of
money received for prisoners used to be entered, and where
the black columns stood out clearly on the not yet yellow
paper: 'Number,' 'Name, Patronymic, Surname,' 'Amount in
Roubles and Kopecks,' 'For What Purpose,' 'Permitted or
Prohibited.' This book, after Kotovsky's cavalry had taken
the city and the fortress prison had been sacked, found its
way along with the rest of the prison records to the market
and was sold there as 'writing paper.'

Now – more than forty years ahead – I was going through
(or am going through?) those tattered sheets with their

fragile edges that seemed to have been eaten away by the sulphuric acid of time.

The poems, to tell the truth, were as bad as ever, but the bits of paper on which they were scratched had retained the traces of my not quite formed handwriting, rather as the cortex retains traces of all the impressions of life, safely guarded by the mechanism of memory, the key to which science has not yet discovered.

What was then 'ahead' has now become 'ago.'

As I examined and sorted out these half-decayed sheets that had by some miracle survived in my files, I seemed to be groping my way through the silent regions of the subconscious into the dark storehouses of dead dreams, trying to revive them; and the power of my imagination was such that all of a sudden, with astonishing, almost tangible authenticity and clarity I saw the interior of a cramped little mud hut, two-thirds full of golden sweet-smelling straw, and the blackened mouth of a whitewashed stove with rounded corners, which made it like the proscenium arch of a tiny theatre with a fairyland backdrop of fire that threw fretful gleams on the figure of the only onlooker, a girl in a homespun skirt that had been dyed with onion skin.

She was sitting on a bench in front of the stove and with rough but pretty hands was teasing tow. A grey spindle hung at the end of the woollen thread, dancing and twirling but just not touching the floor, while the girl's bare foot with very short toes and even shorter, barely visible toe-nails diligently pressed the treadle, and a fluttering breeze blew in my face from the whirling wheel.

Now and then an old woman would clamber down backside forward from the ledge above the stove and, squatting on her haunches, thrust into the fire huge bundles of straw that she could scarcely embrace with her blackened arms.

The straw quickly completed the cycle of combustion.

For a little while it would be swathed in a milky-white opal smoke, which seeped through the porous body of the straw bundle, a second later it would catch fire, seized on all sides by a pure golden flame which seemed to concentrate and preserve all the intolerable heat of July noon in the open fields, scorching the face with its dry healing breath, and then quite suddenly it would turn a gloomy poppy-red, and then darken to poppy-black, grim as paper ashes, and after that the interior of the stove would become wistfully empty, like the stage of a theatre with its decorations taken down and a floor too huge and empty for anything ever to have been presented upon it.

The cramped little hut that just a little while ago had been so full of heat and light was suddenly plunged into a cold and grave-like darkness, so numbing that the young man who was spreading his bits of paper on the scrubbed table under the tiny window found it hard to make out his own handwriting.

That young man – of still quite boyish appearance – was I.

Or to be more exact, he could be I, if only I had the power to resurrect that young self of so long ago. . . . But since I possess no such magic power, I can now, as I write these lines, consider him only as a likeness, an imperfect embodiment of my present conception of myself at that time – if time does, in fact, exist, which has not yet been proved! – a time that has left its sole material trace in the form of tattered sheets of paper scribbled all over with a rotten No. 4 pencil that scratched rather than wrote.

The I that used to be is no more. I have not survived. The pencil has worn down. But the bad verses, scratched on that ash-flimsy paper – here they are! They have survived. Is that not a miracle?

'With a wheat-roll braid her head she wound, my rustic muse, most prettily. Alas, her peasant loveliness, I found, combined with jelly-fish frigidity.

'And yet, with her gay winter eves I spend, while like a worried broody whirs the wheel and speedy spokes their flapping shadows send to roost with squawk and squeal.

'But what to say? I think and smoke. She, mute, to the snowflaked window turns her face. I pant for breath, and so the tardy dawn awoke us once again in long embrace.'

These stanzas, composed in the spirit of the so-called 'South Russian school,' were very much to the liking of the author himself, particularly the place where 'her peasant loveliness combined with jelly-fish frigidity.' These lines were supposed to give an impression of a broad face and of big, somehow frigid and utterly expressionless – violet-coloured – eyes resembling the Black Sea medusa I knew so well or – if you will – the head of Medusa Gorgon, which also suited the somewhat mythological style of those romantic days.

If I were to describe the eyes of that pretty country *tarakutska*[1] today – though why should I? – I should be more inclined to compare them with the sheep's eyes of Vrubel's Pan, the more so since, as far as I remember, there was a crescent moon to be seen through the window. But this did not change matters; the verses were no good at all, like most descriptive verses, and had, in fact, been composed for the sake of the two last lines – absolutely false, because the tardy dawn had never as yet woken the poet and his rustic muse in long embrace. That blameless maiden usually slept on the ledge above the stove with the old woman, while the versifier made himself as comfortable as he could on a piece of sacking spread over the dry clay floor under the table among the dry fowl droppings and bits of straw, with a field bag containing his manuscripts under his head, and covering himself with a much patched sheepskin, which he had managed to obtain at the market in Balta in exchange for an almost new, captured British army greatcoat, which he had drawn from the stores at the Provincial Revolutionary Committee on an authorization from S. Ingulov.

[1] A *tarakutska* is a small dried pumpkin, once a favourite toy of country children in the Ukraine. The same word was used to describe a pretty, round-faced girl.

According to the young man's calculations, his verses were to produce a staggering impression on a certain citizeness whom he had met not long before being sent away on his present assignment, although he had not had time to start up an affair with her or even to see properly what she looked like, and had to console himself with a resolution to make up for lost time immediately on his return to the city.

I write 'citizeness' because in those legendary days such pre-revolutionary words as 'miss' or 'mademoiselle' had been abolished, and the word 'lass,' as a form of address for a young woman, subsequently brought into everyday use by Mayakovsky, had not yet come into fashion and had a purely literary flavour. To say 'young lady' was too Dickensian and old-fashioned and, therefore, absurd and even rude. 'Fair one' was even more absurd. 'Madam' was insultingly derisive. So the only thing left was 'citizeness,' which was well suited to the spirit of the times, because it called to mind Anatole France's *Les Dieux ont soif*, a book which along with Hugo's *Quatre-vingt-treize* was – for lack of any Soviet revolutionary novels – our constant companion, from which we drew all our revolutionary romanticism, aesthetics and terminology.

Nowadays I should simply write 'lass,' but then it was possible to say only 'citizeness,' or, in the last resort, 'young citizeness' – nothing else!

. . . And she was not the *tarakutska* type either. . . .

I – or rather, he – was looking forward to the day when I should suddenly appear in the 'Poets' collective' or on the stage in the 'despatches hall' of the South Russian Telegraph Agency – mature and manly, weather-beaten, full of impressions, slightly ironical, not at all sentimental, perhaps even rude – and throw down on the table covered with red cotton a bundle of new poems and start to recite them by heart – in the declamatory manner, of course! – and not all of them, only the best. First one or two. And then at the enthusiastic request of a delighted but non-paying audience, all the others: twelve lyrical pieces, a rather long revolutionary poem, written in blank verse, a few old sonnets from the 'Iron' cycle, and, of course, above all:

'. . . And the tardy dawn awoke us once again in long embrace.'

It should not be imagined that I or, if you will, that young man, had been sent out into the country for rest and inspiration. The new-born Soviet republic sent its poets on missions of quite a different nature.

He had been sent by a department of the South Russia Telegraph Agency with a mandate from the revolutionary committee to one of the most remote *uyezds* to recruit as many as possible *volost*[1] and village correspondents who would be prepared to send the Agency daily bulletins. For this purpose he had been equipped with a number of stamped forms on which he had only to fill in the name of the recruited correspondent – *volost* or village – and then hand him a short printed list of instructions enumerating his rights and duties.

There were not many rights. On the other hand, there were any number of duties, and chief among them was the duty to fight fearlessly against any abuses perpetrated by the local authorities, any breaches of sacred revolutionary law.

It was this first point in the instructions that saved my life, or, if you will, the life of the hero of this story, which in due course will be told on these pages.

In the mandate issued by the revolutionary committee, everyone, including all institutions and military units, was instructed to render every assistance to the bearer, who had the right to use every means of transport without exception, including aeroplanes, motor rail trolleys, troop trains and railway engines.

[1] *Uyezd* and *volost* were the smaller territorial divisions of a province.

In practice, most of the revolutionary committee's envoys made use of carts, which the local authorities, driven to distraction by the incessant commandeering of draught animals, provided with all the unwillingness in the world.

I gave him my flesh and blood and living soul, but I did not wish to give him my name for fear of becoming like the man who lost his shadow.

I called him Rurik Pcholkin. Was that not a suitable name for a young Russian, born at the end of the nineteenth century, just before the Revolution, when for some unknown reason there was suddenly a fashion for such princely names as Igor, Gleb, Oleg, Rurik, Svyatoslav?

After that I sighed with relief, having from now on shifted all my cares on to another's shoulders.

Rurik Pcholkin would for days on end jolt around the *uyezd* on a cart, calling at the local *volost* offices, and at each office he would show his mandate, and the chairman of the *volost* Executive Committee would find a billet for him in some hut or cottage, to which he would be accompanied by the village policeman, who would tap on the window with an elder-wood truncheon, his symbol of authority.

'Hi there, missus! You've got a representative to stay with you!'

'May your guts fall out! Why do you always come bothering me? Can't you put the man up with someone else for a change?'

'Can't be done. It's your turn.'

'Curse your father and all his brood!'

After which, having stood for a while on the flat porous stone of the doorstep, that seemed to have taken root in the earth, Pcholkin thumbed down the iron latch and entered the dark passage, then groped his way into the even darker interior of the hut, which reeked of hen's feathers, dry clay and wheat chaff.

When his eyes, after the bright evening light outside,

eventually grew accustomed to the darkness, he saw in front of him an old woman in a checked homespun skirt and with all the dignity he possessed removed his cap from his shaven pale-blue head, trying to produce the impression of a man of substance, who knew what he was about when it came to country customs. Modestly lowering his eyes, he made a sweeping sign of the cross before the ikon, then performed an exaggeratedly low bow to the mistress of the house.

'But you don't really believe in God, do you?' the old woman asked, not without a touch of sarcasm.

'I do, granny.'

'Well, you can certainly tell lies. Sit down on that bench. That's where you'll sleep.'

'Thank you kindly.'

'Why, he's just a puppy! Ought to be holding on to his mummy's skirts but he's already travelling about as a representative. Beg your pardon, sir, but what business is it you represent? If it's commandeering grain, you're too late. They've cleaned us out already. And if it's home-brew, we don't go in for that kind of thing.'

'No, I'm a journalist.'

The old woman pursed her wrinkled lips contemptuously, like someone tying the strings of a tobacco pouch.

'So you're a clerk, eh?'

And to explain to her what a journalist was proved utterly impossible.

Meanwhile the pretty *tarakutska*, clutching a bowl of blue poppy seed to her bosom and burning with curiosity, was climbing down from the stove, planting one bare heel after another carefully on each ledge in turn. She pretended not to take the slightest interest in the young baby-faced representative; her round face was smeared with cucumber pickle-water, and just by the small flesh-pink mouth a white cucumber seed had stuck to her firm crimson cheek.

It was more or less the same in every village, and in each

one Pcholkin enjoyed staying for a day or two or, perhaps, even three on the 'as long as your cheek lasts' principle.

After the meagre fare of the city he was here able to fill himself up with grey wheaten rolls, cubes of salted bacon fat, pickled green tomatoes, broth, hominy and other coarse, but filling country food to which he was treated by the women, who eventually decided to put up with their lodger, a half-starved specimen from the provincial centre, where people lived on ration cards that had mainly symbolic significance because almost nothing was available on them.

. . . This was soon after the capture of Perekop. . . .

Had there been men in charge of the houses where he stayed he might not have received such gentle treatment, but by some unwritten law the village elder would nearly always send the lonely representative to the house of a widow, a soldier's wife or an old woman who felt the lack of male company, so that as far as nourishment was concerned an assignment to the country was rather like being sent off nowadays to a health resort.

By the same unwritten law, if a representative stayed on for a few extra days, he would lend his landlady a hand with her work, performing some manly task. In short, he would not eat his bread for nothing.

Pcholkin did not possess sufficient physical strength and, being a thoroughly urban individual, was not accustomed to physical labour, so he was not much use to his landladies, but he never refused work; in fact, painfully aware of his uselessness, he actually asked for something to do and was glad to scratch about with a fork in the dry, tobacco-like layers of old dung in the backyard, or hump to the wattle-fenced threshing floor two or three not very heavy sacks of bran or corn cobs. At least, that was something!

He was of pleasant appearance, dark-eyed, and his shaven head told the tender-hearted women that he had not long since had the typhus, and they were kind to him and fed him and even provided him with dark-green sandpaper-like leaves of home-grown tobacco, which he cut into fine strips with a penknife and smoked with pleasure, sometimes using thin maize leaves instead of paper to roll his cigarettes in. Such favours he was able to repay in kind. In his knapsack he always carried a small supply of needles in little black packets, a couple of reels of No. 40 thread, a dozen mother-of-pearl buttons on a silvery strip of cardboard and other cheap draper's articles, acquired at the market in Odessa specially for purposes of barter. This scientific term has long since gone out of fashion with us and is to be found only in textbooks, but in those days it was the hub on which the whole economy turned.

At his place of work a citizen would receive his food ration. Part of this he would barter for articles that in their turn could be bartered in the country for farm produce. This he used partly to keep himself alive and partly to exchange for certain necessaries, which in their turn were converted at the same market into other, less essential articles on the basis of the laws of supply and demand, price fluctuations and other subtleties of the economic life of the epoch of war communism. And so it went on until what had been acquired was ultimately used up, whereupon the individual tightened his belt and waited patiently for next month's rations or took to market some article of domestic use.

In the countryside this barter was much more lively than in the city, where people were mercilessly fleeced by all sorts of middlemen, profiteers and speculators, and in the country it yielded – in scientific terms – a far higher percentage of profit on basic capital.

In short, as Mayakovsky put it, 'we learned dialectics not from Hegel,' and our understanding of economics certainly did not come from reading Marx.

It should not be imagined, however, that these assignments to the country were one long round of pleasure. Not at

111

all. They were very dangerous. The provinces were swarming with unmopped-up remnants of the Denikin. Wrangel, Petlyura and Makhno forces and the bands of other Ukrainian local leaders such as Zabolotny, Zelyony, Angel and even a woman called Maruska Nikiforova, who ruled the remote by-ways, attacked isolated village soviets, commandeered carts and horses, murdered food requisitioners, village Communists, and various instructors from the Provincial Revolutionary Committee and, later, the Provincial Executive Committee, sent out from the centre to organize an increase in the sowing areas, which was absolutely essential because ominous warnings were pouring in from all sides of the approach of a year of bad harvests and famine.

The local bands sabotaged the work of restoring the economy and spread discontent. They were difficult to eradicate. Operating, as they did, along the frontier, they could easily, if hard pressed, cross the Dniester and take refuge in monarchist Rumania.

An assignment to the countryside could, therefore, without exaggeration be equated with being sent to the front line, to the most advanced positions.

It was in such circumstances that the young instructor from the South Russia Telegraph Agency set out to recruit his correspondents in such remote areas that, if he was disposed of by one of the bands, it was highly unlikely that anyone would hear anything about it. Yet, he was entitled to carry no arms except a pencil, and in an emergency could count only on his eloquence, fleetness of foot, or a miracle.

His assignment was almost completed. He had only two or three more *volosts* to cover and he would be able to return to the centre.

The correspondents were recruited mainly from the rural intelligentsia, district clerks and village schoolteachers, young greenhorns like himself, who almost before they had completed their teachers' training had gone off to the war as second-grade volunteers and become ensigns, only to be pestered by the humiliating gibe: 'A hen's no bird and an ensign's no officer.'

At first glance the task appeared simple. He had only to have a heart-to-heart chat with someone of his own age, perhaps even an old front-line comrade, talk him round in no time, hand him his authorization with its round Soviet seal bearing the emblem of the hammer and sickle and ears of corn, give him the printed instructions and jog along quietly to the next village, yawning and making up in his head verses which it would be so pleasant later to write down where he stayed the night with the spinning wheel whirring by the light of a wick soaked in grease or even a burning pine-splinter, from which the ribbon-like embers fell, spluttering, into the trough of water on the floor beneath.

Why, I actually remember those pine-splinter lights! And yet only a short time ago television showed us a panorama of the moon transmitted from one of our artificial satellites!

Not all the teachers and village clerks, however, would agree to become Soviet correspondents; some of them needed much persuading; some would gently but firmly refuse on various plausible grounds. Either they were not well enough educated to write for the press, or they were afraid to disgrace themselves or, quite frankly, they were worried about the possible consequences – Pcholkin could guess what.

Such hints would sometimes upset Pcholkin very much and he would long to get away from this godforsaken place, where he might so easily be rubbed out of existence without anyone knowing that he had died a hero's death for the young Soviet republic.

One day the transport chief of an *uyezd* executive committee, wishing to economize, departed from the usual practice of giving the holder of a mandate a cart to himself, and put Pcholkin on a spring *britzka* with a comrade who was being sent out to some of the remoter *volosts* of the *uyezd* to agitate for expansion of the sowing area and to fight kulak influence over the middle and poor peasants.

Apparently he, too, had been sent to the country by the indefatigable Sergei Ingulov.

This comrade was sitting in the office of the chairman of the *uyezd* executive committee – table covered with velvet raspberry-coloured table-cloth, carafe of yellowish water, slop basin and cracked tumbler – with his head in the pages of a Moscow illustrated journal called *The Atheist*, which came out under the editorship of our former Odessa Bolshevik Yemelyan Yaroslavsky, and his face was entirely hidden behind the amazing and unprecedented drawings of an artist with the strange and rather sinister pseudonym of Moor. These drawings were caricatures portraying Lord Sabaoth himself in an old-fashioned, music-hall pince-nez with a halo round his bald head, a rabbi with long sidelocks and a black-striped *tallith* on his shoulders, and beside him, a mullah in a turban who looked like a clove of garlic, and finally, one of our Russian Orthodox priests with drunkard's eyes and a strawberry nose, and the verses of the first proletarian poet Demyan Bedny – altogether the kind of blasphemy to which not everyone had at that time grown accustomed, and which seemed so monstrous that it would have been no surprise if the heavens had suddenly opened and from a black thundercloud a zigzag of dazzling white lightning had struck and burned to ashes the godless journal along with its editor, caricaturists, poet and all its annual subscribers.

Sensing that he was being watched, the comrade lowered his magazine, and suddenly it turned out that he was himself a priest, with a narrow beard, a long, slightly pock-marked nose and impudent, cockerel's eyes under the arrogantly soaring brows of a prophet. A steel-rimmed pince-nez with its black cord attached behind the ear, under lank streaks of hair, was perched on his nose much lower than it should have been, and this imparted an aggressive air to the whole face.

'Well, young man,' he said nasally, 'so you are the person they have thrust upon me as a travelling companion? Personally, I prefer to travel without company – solo, as it were – but since our young Soviet republic has not yet sufficient means of transport to provide every citizen with his own cart, I have no objection to your taking a seat in my boneshaker. I warn you, however, that I can't bear being cramped, so if you cause me any discomfort and, particularly, if you weary me with attempts at conversation, I shall immediately request you to leave the vehicle and continue your journey in the manner of a pedestrian.'

It turned out that this was the 'red priest' of whom Pcholkin had already heard, and who was now voluntarily going off to the remote *volosts* to agitate for an expansion of the sowing area. Besides this, however, he had another aim, unknown to the central authorities. He was an advocate of the idea of a new revolutionary Christian Church, conjured up quite recently in his own imagination, and had now decided to make use of his assignment to bring about an ecclesiastical coup, reshuffle the Orthodox hierarchy from top to bottom, from the great princes of the Church to the local country parsons, who, in his opinion, had defiled themselves with all kinds of worldly vice, and to raise on the ruins of the old Church which he had overthrown the banner of a new, purely mystical Christianity of his own making.

To drive in the same *britzka* with him was sheer torture.

He turned out to be a mistrustful, capricious, overconfident man, exceedingly vain, and with an extremely high opinion of his own person, which under the old regime had not been duly appreciated by the leaders of the Russian Orthodox Church, that pack of 'consistorial rats,' who had constantly worked intrigues against him and kept him down, not wishing to consecrate him to the office of bishop, whereas he considered himself the Lord's elect, a militant apostle with a fiery sword in his hand.

The purple ruddiness of his long hairy neck reminded one of a turkey.

As soon as they set out, he began to talk and argue, picking on every word and even interjection of his companion. Having got it out of the young man that he was a poet, he launched into a tirade of venomous ridicule against modern poetry and painting, calling the pictures of the impressionists and the Barbizon school scrambled eggs and onion, and Vrubel and Čiurlionis, whom the young man worshipped, artists from the word 'artful.' And all the time he pressed his long bony body against his companion, who only just managed to keep his seat and was in much pain from the iron rail grinding into his hindquarters.

But when the priest began to lambast Mayakovsky, saying he had no ear and was not to be compared with the poet Apukhtin, the young man could bear it no longer and bellowed at the top of his voice that the priest himself did not know a damn thing about art and was a dyed-in-the-wool conservative and counter-revolutionary, and that there was no place for such types in the new, communist society of today, and that he had no wish to share his company any longer.

With these words Pcholkin jumped out of the *britzka* and for a time stomped along in furious independence, his army boots drumming on the iron-hard ruts and humps of the frozen road, amid the equally frozen fields, which though winter was nearing its end were still completely free of snow and in places showed the green of sickly winter wheat, ominously bare and blackened, presaging a bad harvest and perhaps even famine.

He soon worked his feet into blisters, however, and was compelled to resume his seat with a pretence that nothing had happened. This performance was repeated several times and a particularly stormy scene took place when the priest called Bunin a puny decadent because in one of his poems there was a line in which the 'lapwings wept' and another with 'violet mud on the ploughland.'

'Decadent rubbish! How can birds weep and how on

earth could there be such a thing as violet mud? Where have you ever seen violet mud? Contrived, pretentious, modernist!'

'But he's a classic, a classic!' Pcholkin cried, almost in tears. 'I won't let you speak of the Academician like this. After all, I was his pupil.'

'Anyone can see that you were his pupil. "Violet mud!"'

When they at last reached a place where they could stay the night, Pcholkin flatly refused to go any further with him and found himself separate lodgings.

A rumour immediately flashed round the village that a terrible 'red priest' had arrived from the centre and would the following day, Sunday, take the service at the village church and preach a sermon. For some reason this greatly alarmed the villagers.

When he arrived in church that morning to find out what was going on, Pcholkin saw his companion of the day before in the pulpit, adorned in Easter robes of silk brocade – somewhat tattered but still shimmeringly white and elegant – with a cross in his bony hand which he was holding up over the Sunday-best kerchiefs of the frightened old women in the front row.

The local parson, a kindly old man, stood beside him at a loss what to do with his small childish hands and staring in confusion now at his feet in their worn dung-stained peasant boots, now upwards at the all-seeing eye in a radiant triangle, crudely painted in the domed roof by a local artist against a background of a faded blue and starry sky, in the middle of which, on a heap of clouds and looking rather like a billowing cloud himself, was seated the long-haired old man of Sabaoth, listening angrily to what was being said below by the visiting preacher.

To begin with the preacher talked of expanding the sowing area, growing more and more heated as he went on, and suddenly, eyeing the local parson as a cock eyes a grain of corn, he climbed straight on to his favourite hobby horse and without the slightest restraint began to fulminate against the hated princes of the so-called holy, so-called Orthodox, so-called equal apostolic Church.

'What kind of apostles are these!' he cried in mounting fury. 'The apostles of Christ ate from wooden bowls but they had golden heads on their shoulders, and yet these, pardon the expression, self-styled apostles, have cups of gold and their heads are made of wood!'

He tapped expressively with his bony fingers on the wooden rail of the pulpit, and then brandished his cross at the trembling local parson.

'Glutton, drunkard, adulterer!'

As the final imprecation rang out, the parson's wife, who was wearing a black silk dress and standing in the place of honour just under the pulpit, turned pale, then came out in red spots and grew very agitated, but the women calmed her and the men in their best white, very long sheepskins with black collars or army greatcoats with frayed yellow edges – Ukrainians and Moldavians – recently returned home after the defeat of Baron Wrangel and the Polish war, stood in silence, their moustaches drooping grimly, and to Pcholkin something seemed to flit through the air – it may have been a shadow, a breath of wind, but whatever it was, it was so terrifying that his legs sagged under him and to escape the hostile glances directed at him from all sides he edged his way out into the porch and returned to his lodgings.

At dawn he was awoken by a gentle, persistent tapping on the window. It was the young schoolmaster he had the day before recruited as a *volost* correspondent.

'Colleague,' the schoolmaster said in a whisper. 'Take my advice and don't waste time. Get out of here before it's too late. I've borrowed a cart from some good friends of ours. It'll take you as far as the next *volost*. You must get out of here. Run while you've got the chance.'

Pcholkin detected in his colleague's voice something that sent a shiver all the way up his spine. It was that same

shadow of death that he had sensed so acutely in the church
the previous day.

In those days people had learned to take a hint, half a hint,
half a glance, half a sigh, even half a silence.

Pcholkin stuck his bag of papers under his arm and in a
minute, bouncing up and down on the hard boards of the
cart that no one had had time to spread with straw, he was
rolling away down the hard village track. It began to
grow light, and soon all was visible. It was a cold, dry gloomy
day. All around stretched the black, frozen fields with ricks
of old straw and windmills flapping along on the horizon.

Having recovered a little and looked around, Pcholkin, as
was his habit, began to make up a poem about the surrounding countryside. This time he personified it.

'Spring in a homespun shirt, her tresses flying loose, runs
across the boundless fields and where'er she goes a poisonous
green upon the steppeland blackness glows.'

Barefooted spring was just another version of the pretty
tarakutska, his 'provincial muse,' and was not quite in keeping with his feelings of alarm that simply would not be
dispelled, although the menacing tower of the village church
had by now dropped out of sight behind the hill.

He remembered the candles gleaming in the cottage windows, and the old women praying fervently in church for
God to send snow to moisten the fields. This was more in
keeping with his mood.

'When spring is near, in every hut we hear a prayer for
snow to slake the field and keep the drought away, and
round the ikon candles glow. Then each old dame must pray
and cross her sullen brow, and every child at ikon bow. . . .'

The verse was just beginning to sing, when all of a sudden
a group of horsemen rose up in front of him and barred
his way. At first he thought it was a squadron of Red

Cavalry and actually noted with pleasure that the uniforms were much better nowadays; all alike and with brand new stars on their caps.

But at that moment a horse's head, straining at the bit, let out a loud neigh above him, spluttering grass-green foam in his face, and the handsome commander of the group in a white cap with long earflaps and gold braid at the back leaned down from his saddle and with a string of curses addressed Pcholkin.

'Who are you? A representative?'

'I'm a journalist.'

'Now then, you pen-pushing rat! Get out of that cart!'

'A journalist is not at all what you think it is,' Pcholkin whispered with a forced smile.

'How d'you know what I think?'

'I write for a newspaper.'

'For a newspaper? Kick his arse for him, lads. Look at him – thinks he can run things in our village like in his own home. Give him a cart whenever he wants one!'

'Comrade, this is a misunderstanding. It's my right. I have a mandate from the revolutionary committee.'

'Why, it's one of the comrades, and still alive! You red-arsed louse! Take him away into the corn and the cart can go back where it came from.'

It had all happened so quickly. And now, as he stood among the uncut stalks of last year's maize, which closed in upon him with their sword-like leaves, reducing the horizon to a mere two paces, and as he felt the carbine butts reeking of kerosene and oil jabbing him roughly in the back, Pcholkin realized that he had fallen into the hands of a band disguised in Red Army uniform, and that he was being led away to be shot.

Terror seized his soul, his mind went dark, his body weakened, his internal organs ceased to obey the orders of the nerve centres that a sudden spasm had paralysed, and he began shamefully and irrestrainably to empty his bowels while the leader of the band, perched in his saddle with its velvet, brigade commander's saddle-cloth, took the papers out of Pcholkin's bag and casually read them aloud until he came across the printed instruction, which caught his attention because of the clause about combatting abuses by the local Soviet authorities and breaches of the law.

Oddly enough, it was this that saved Pcholkin.

'Wait a minute, lads,' the leader said. 'First make sure he's not a sheeny, and if he isn't, let him go and good riddance. And let him not poke his nose in any more where he's not wanted or cross our path again.'

Having ascertained in extremely rough and ready fashion that Pcholkin was not a Jew, the lads tucked his bag of papers under his arm, drove a knee into his backside and sent him on his way with a few warning bullets that whistled tenderly over his head and curved away steeply into the ominously dark sky of the March morning.

Any one of those sharp conical bullets might have made a mistake and hit him in the head and shattered forever that divine world of love, beauty and poetry it contained, the unique, inimitable, precious life of Pcholkin, with all its verses, his own and other people's, born and as yet unborn, or only just understood, such as, for instance, the magical mad lines of Velemir Khlebnikov or Nikolai Burlyuk:

'The face of vengeance floats amid the stars, snake-like in agitation writhes, a head cut off with knives. . . . O, spirit of delight in darkness! Queen no less than Plague! . . . No, the bucket on the yoke touched not the shoulder. The long curls hung like the notes of a violin.'

Only such mad lines could arise in the brain at the moment of violent death!

'We drink water – some from a glass, but some with lips pressed to the living stream amid spring mists as we pass by midnight shores. No stars are seen. Yet bright the dusk that falls within these silver walls. I met no woman rider in the fields and found but traces of the foam. But suddenly through the mist again I hear a whisper and see the willow sway where vernal torrents rush with flying mane. . . .'

Only when he was a hair's breadth from destruction amid the black, frozen fields of his wild country could there have flashed through Pcholkin's memory those divine sounds:

'With gentle sigh and stealthy tread, through the mists of troubled days, o'er the plains and narrow gullies of my ancient motherland, o'er the unploughed fields, o'er the murmuring rushes, o'er the streams and marshes, every night there passes someone sick and weary in whose blue eyes there slumbers a portentous warmth. Thus, in the cloak of night he stands, then splashes down the stream, and sometimes he by chance may leave a hoofmark on the sands.'

I describe nature – stars, forest, frost, sea, mountains, wind, people. These are all my colours. But are not literature, poetry, created by the genius of man, a part of nature? Why may I not make use of them, their luminous colours, particularly as I have to put the stars into words, while the lines of these mad and brilliant poets are already in words, there for the taking – so take them as part of eternal nature and mould them into your free, unfettered prose! . . .

. . . with all his passions, conjectures, his constant thirst for love and his burning impatience to return to the town and meet that girl, that 'young citizeness' who had promised him bliss. . . .

Azrael, sent for his soul, flew overhead on ashen wings, zigzagged back and forth soaring and plunging, like a huge buzzing wasp, but missed his mark. . . .

'How afraid I was! How fast I fled! But with a sudden cloud swift Hermes hid my head and plucked me from death's all-engulfing shroud.'

Pcholkin ran like a hare from the hunters, tripping and

falling, breaking the hard stalks of the maize that beat him about the head, clutching his bag to his chest and adjusting his dress as he ran, and he went on running till the sound of trotting hooves died away in the distance.

'A hoofmark on the sands.'

And once again the world was still. He was alive, but his murdered soul lay on the iron-hard earth amid the broken maize stalks awaiting resurrection, just as another fear-blackened soul of his was lying by the gun emplacements near Smorgon, and somewhere else, yet another soul that had departed agonizingly from his body on a bed in the typhus hospital to the beating of Buddhist drums under the sacred lamaist writings that looked like Mendeleyev's table of elements.

And they would all most certainly be resurrected because they were immortal.

Having left his soul lying spreadeagled amid the withered maize stalks in expectation of resurrection, and sensing in his weakened body the birth of a new soul, Pcholkin set off across the black-green fields, avoiding all villages and farmsteads and trying to reach the local town as quickly as possible without being seen by anyone.

It took him two days to reach Balta, carefully avoiding the populated areas and spending the night in straw stacks capped with snow and in lonely barns on the heaped corn cobs with their pebble-like, amber-yellow seeds, and feeding on the mangels left behind in the fields after the harvest.

'I washed at night in a yard all frozen up with stars, each ray bright and hard as salt upon an axe. . . . Like salt a star melts and chars the icy water blacker still. So is death made cleaner, and saltier ill, juster the earth – and more terrible.'

Repeating these lines of Mandelstam's he wandered on alone under the huge lowering sky, under the cordite clouds that gathered overhead until they were heavy as slabs of anthracite, ready at any moment to fall and crush him.

And all this – strange to say – seemed to him wonderful, magnificent, like a work of unprecedented revolutionary art, full of divine meaning and supernatural beauty.

Fear had made the poor fellow quite mad.

It began to blow bitterly cold. Snow fell and began to whirl about, mingling earth and sky. He stopped and in his imagination it seemed to him that this was the Lord of Hosts himself who 'with frowning brow and dreadful visage blue' had yielded to man's prayers and 'given the storms white seed upon the earth to strew.'

'Amid the storm, in trembling fear I stand alone before thee, Lord, ingloriously to perish here upon a snowbound road.'

In this case God was merely a version of Pushkin's Peter: 'His visage grim, his movements swift. How splendid he is, like the thunder of the Lord.' Pcholkin had enriched the visage grim with the iron blueness of the snowstorm, but his inglorious death amid the snowbound roads and particularly the strewing of white seed sounded fairly original.

Subsequently – many years ahead – I came to the conclusion that there has only ever been and ever will be in Russia one immortal poet, the national genius, bearing different names.

In our own time it is the same. Within my memory there have been several.

Even when on the verge of destruction Pcholkin had not been able to rid his mind for an instant of the image of the young woman, the 'citizeness' who had wounded his soul and was pursuing him irremovably, giving him no rest day or night, like an ever-present thought, exhausting the

124

brain with her nearness, reality, almost tangibility, the authenticity of delightful details, which nevertheless could not satisfy his desire for possession; because by now he loved her passionately, while she, of course, had no idea that this was so and had probably forgotten all about him, having seen him only once in the turmoil of the 'dispatches hall' and the 'poets' collective,' where they had exchanged only a few quite insignificant phrases.

And yet he loved her, more dearly and more desperately every day – or perhaps this was only his imagination? – and she was before his eyes day and night, and even at the moment of death, irremovable and passionately desired, in her white fur cap with very long earflaps that hung down over her breast like two plaits reaching to her belt.

When, one day she took off this Siberian cap there turned out to be another underneath, a curly-black cap of hair that she shook out because it had become matted.

By now he had forgotten what she had been wearing – perhaps a soldier's quilted jacket with sleeves that were much too long for her and that she turned up revealing her wrists and small brown hands with their roughly clipped white-spotted nails; her slim but sturdy figure was girdled with an officer's belt with rings in it, her threadbare woollen skirt barely covered her knees, her legs were wrapped in black soldier's puttees, and she wore small button-over shoes, almost like a child's, on her feet.

A brown, earthily opaque face, perfect features, rather forbidding or, at any rate, uncompromising eyes, a small mole like a blue powder scar on her tender cheek and a tawny fluff above her virginally pale lips, which were sensual yet at the same time deceptively innocent.

Those lips were constantly before his eyes and all the time they seemed to be coming nearer to his own, and they lasted and lasted and lasted whether he was sleeping or waking, like an unending kiss that gives no satisfaction.

That was his first impression of her. Later her appearance

changed a bit. In winter she must have had typhoid or typhus, and when she reappeared in the 'dispatches hall' – much thinner – and took off her white fur cap with long earflaps, the head that emerged was as clean-shaven as a raw recruit's and came out of her cap like a nut out of its shell, a small, well-proportioned head with firm ears, one of which was stained with school ink, and a white, almost light-blue scalp, gleaming through the uneven trails left by the careless clippers of the hospital barber.

It was known that she worked as a typist in the administrative department of the province CHEKA, attended the Party school at the department of public education and was studying to enter the Sverdlov University in Moscow.

Apparently in order to broaden her knowledge of literature she conscientiously attended the 'poets' collective' and the 'dispatches hall' of the South Russia Telegraph Agency. where propagandists and writers used to speak every day. She always came alone, sat down in the front row with the independent and rather scornful air of one belonging to the upper class and listened to the stories and poems attentively but without expressing any feelings whatever.

'Citizeness, this is not the first time I have noticed you here,' Pcholkin addressed her one day. 'You seem to be an admirer of poetry? Or perhaps, of poets?'

'I come here to raise my general level of development,' she replied.

'Does it need raising?'

'Of course.'

'Do you like my poems?' he asked sternly but not without a touch of gallantry.

'Yes, I do,' she replied simply.

'Flattered. And do you like me?'

'Yes.'

This confession at once destroyed his conception of her as a local Théronigne de Méricourt, a fury of the revolution, a dry Party woman who despised petit-bourgeois Bohemianism and repudiated all frivolous attitudes to love. He was, however, disappointed by the light-heartedness of her response to his advances, so he entered her in the list of his conquests and lost a great deal of his former interest in her. His victory had been too easy. But he did not drop her altogether; he merely put her aside to prolong the pleasure of getting to know her better.

'I trust you are not a poet yourself?' he remarked carelessly.

'Your trust is justified,' she answered, and just at that moment he at last noticed the most delightful feature of her face, that small misty blue mole, like a powder scar under the skin on her brown cheek; it was so well suited to her close-cropped head, which did not make her a bit like a boy but, on the contrary, only emphasized her femininity.

'We may meet again soon,' he said casually.

'I think we may,' she replied, surprised that he had not offered to see her home.

'Greetings and fraternity!' he said, raising his hand above his head.

She gave him a farewell smile in reply.

He felt he had won the day, and only when he awoke in the middle of the night on his iron bedstead in his unheated room with hoarfrost glittering like diamonds on the wallpaper, did he realize what a fool he had been. He shouldn't have played around, he should have struck while the iron was hot. Mentally he was already holding her weightless arm and kissing her, while forestalling events by making up the lines:

'When your hand, so light and fair, in my hand quivers like the strings of some submissive viol, those tight-pressed lips persist as does the bow that sings like bee above the rose-bud of a smile.'

The 'rose-bud of a smile' was stolen, of course, from the arsenal of his friend Yuri Olesha.

Pcholkin saw that pale rose-bud of her smile, and the little mole on her cheek grew to the size of a bee hovering above her. Fool that he was! Instead of imagining all this he could have been enjoying himself in a very real and tangible way.

'Oh, blessed is the poet,' he went on composing in the darkness of his icy room with hoarfrost on his pillow, 'but wise – not he who counts his heart-beats then writes of the "kiss that sings," but he whom passion leaves no power to say such things.'

He could indeed find no verbal expression for his passion and was quite prepared, despite the lateness of the hour and the state of siege, to run to her that very minute, but not only was he ignorant of her address, he had not even inquired her name.

He could not go to sleep again. He was experiencing the feeling that the great Russian poet who at one time in the nineteenth century bore the name of Pushkin, defined with frightening insight: 'My soul is envenomed with you.' Yes, his soul was envenomed, poisoned. It was festering. He could think of nothing but her. She stood immovable before him with moonlight in the narrow whites of her eyes, the mistress of all his thoughts and desires. He had no idea how he would last out till their next meeting. But the following day he was ordered to leave at once on his mission to the country. It could not have entered his head to refuse because any official assignment was at that time treated as part of one's Sacred Revolutionary Duty.

The Revolution itself commanded men's lives in those days.

. . . He stood amid the whirling snow that plastered his face with wet flakes and wrapped the surrounding country in a swirling opacity. After wandering all night without any sense of direction, he at dawn found himself among the backyards of a village. He had no strength left. He was ready to lie down under the snow-flecked fence and sleep forever. Scarcely aware of what he was doing, he tapped on a small window where a light was showing. Someone let him in and he at once collapsed like a dead man on a pile of dry maize leaves in the golden warmth of the stove, and when he awoke in the morning a well-washed patch of spring sky was showing blue in the window and it turned out that he was only a few miles from Balta, whose windows and church crosses he could see shining and shimmering like mica in the sunlit mist.

In the yard, amid the heaps of dung which stung the nostrils like ammonia, he was dazzled by the mirror-like arteries of trickling streams. There was a smell of damp black earth in the air and the boom of church-bells could be heard in the distance.

When he reached the outskirts of the town, he saw the silk brocade banners of a strange church procession, which included the red banners of the local Soviet organizations, and heard the singing of a church choir in some incomprehensible way blended with the sounds of a brass band.

'What festival is it today?' he asked a woman, who was carrying on her shoulder a thick, marble-like slab of bacon fat half wrapped up in a clean cloth.

'This is no festival,' she replied sternly in Ukrainian. 'It's them Soviet authorities and the church burying that Red priest – the one who's a hero – and two or three food requisitioners and some clerk or other from the town of Odessa that were killed a few days ago by Ataman Zabolotny's band in the village of Ozhila. Had you not heard?'

'No, I hadn't,' Pcholkin said, scarcely aware of the sound of his own voice.

'Well, everybody else has! They were all disguised as Red Army men. They galloped into the village in the morning, dragged them out of their huts and shot them all on the spot. Then away they went across the Dniester into Rumania.'

The funeral tolling floated over the town – thin bells striking A-flat between long, suspenseful pauses – and the sorrowful chanting mingled with the notes of the brass band, the laboured gasps of the trumpets, and the roll of a Turkish drum, and there was a cloying, metallic scent of benzoin incense in the air, and Pcholkin stood clutching his bag of poems to his chest, as though he were attending his own funeral. Little did he know that in the Odessa *Izvestia* there had already appeared a report of the death in action of the poet-journalist Pcholkin, and that his father, old Pcholkin, who had stopped to look at the fresh newspaper pasted up on the hoarding and had read the report, had at first sat down on the pavement, waving his arms as though trying to swim, then rolled over with his face to the wall of a house with his legs drawn up to his chest as though to find a comfortable attitude for sleep, while his old civil servant's cap, flattened like a pancake, badgeless, its leather band stained with sweat, slipped off his head, revealing a purple-red bald spot, while the angel of death, who had arrived with a flutter of black wings just in time, quickly and almost painlessly – like a good dentist – extracted his soul, or rather unscrewed it with a powerful twist of his blood-stained hand, and his body began slowly and blissfully to cool, and it cooled until its temperature was equal to that of the surrounding air and the blue lava slabs of the pavement – about fifteen degrees Celsius – and later continued to assume the temperature of its immediate environment – the hospital reception room, the municipal mortuary, the unheated empty church and finally the cemetery earth which rattled down on the lid of the cheap lime-wood coffin that had been issued free of charge by the local authorities to his neighbours. . . .

It was only on the third day after the funeral that his son, still knowing nothing of what had happened, returned from his mission and suddenly learned everything and was horrified, and now with a feeling of horror at the great chasm of death that had opened before him, with a feeling of independence, of liberation, of heart-rending loneliness, and of passionate belated affection for his father, stood over the clay mound of the grave, which was already beginning to settle and subside under two or three miserable wire wreaths with paper flowers and grey calico ribbons and the newspaper-like inscriptions that had also been provided free by the local authorities.

Beside this new grave there was an old grave with an iron cross painted in 'birch-tree' colours, which seemed to have been welded together out of samovar smoke-pipes, and an imitation marble scroll, on which was painted in glossy black letters the tender name of Pcholkin's mother.

Here, too, lurching in opposite directions, stood the old blackened oak crosses over the scarcely visible mounds of his grandmother and grandfather, whom Pcholkin could not remember. He could hardly remember his mother either. In his imagination she existed as a lady in a hat with a feather in it, and with a sweet but somehow abstractly severe, frozen face, and it always seemed incomprehensible that after her death she had not ceased to exist but was still lying there under the earth, a carefully dressed lady in a whalebone corset with a frill round the hem of her long moire dress, satin shoes of the flimsiest design, and a strip of paper on her icy brow.

He stood alone among the long needles of the new-born cemetery grass sprouting out of ground scattered with grey embers from the censers that had swung during the funeral service, and he experienced such tormenting pity and love and, above all, such a sense of inexpiable guilt towards his father, whom, without realizing it, he had been steadily killing all his life, by having measles, diphtheria and scarlet fever, by swimming too far out to sea, by being at the war, where every bullet, every shell splinter that whistled harmlessly past the son killed the father a thousand times, inevitably, every hour, every second, where the poisonous German asphyxiating gas, phosgene, tormented him at night and the mere thought of cyanogen chloride slowly destroyed his lungs and made him spit blood – while his son was quite oblivious to all this and took life as it came, rarely thinking of death, and died a dozen times without regrets while at the same time delighting in this life, in the inimitable grandeur of the age in which he had had the good fortune to be born – the age of wars and revolutions.

As he bowed his head he seemed to see through the layers of yellow and black earth the sharp outlines of his father's coffin with tassels at the corners and an awkward, ochre-painted lid decorated with metal 'Palestine wreathes' clamped down over his father's white sunken face with its blackened eyelids.

Now that he was quite alone in this world he experienced a strange feeling of liberation that, while taking his breath away, did not give him the freedom he desired but, on the contrary, bound him to the earth with the terrible force of a grief even the possibility of which he could not hitherto have conceived. And yet, this was freedom, and to turn it into complete liberation – perfect and ideal – he must free himself of everything material that bound him to his father. Of everything except his love for his father. That was in-eradicable.

It was an act of despair, the exultation of self-burning, when in his father's musty, dilapidated little room, where the very wallpaper still retained various dry, old-mannish smells, there suddenly appeared two rag-and-bone men still in their traditional bowler-hats but with Soviet-style Tolstoy blouses under their long Jewish coats, two survivors from the ruins of the old world, and began to value the dead man's property, holding up to the light the worn, frayed trousers, the tussore-silk jacket and the pointed ankle-boots with hook fastenings and oval, stratified holes worn in the soles, and then tossed them into a heap on the cloth spread out on the floor to receive them.

Pcholkin stood alienatedly leaning against the door, smoking a home-made cigarette. Tears streamed down his youthful cheeks. The ecstatic pleasure of complete freedom that had opened before him like a yawning precipice bounded in his throat and he watched motionlessly as various domestic articles dropped on to the heap: a rattling chess-board, yellowed collars and 'composition' cuffs, shirt-fronts, an ink-stand clogged with dried-up flies, the velvet-covered family album with its brass clasps, an enlarged photograph of his mother in a black wooden frame – yes, yes, even his mother's photograph as well! Let him be left with absolutely nothing! Let him embark upon a new life, liberated from all feelings and things!. . .

Here I part company with Pcholkin. . . .

'When parting words are spoken who can say how long? Who can say at cockcrow what morning wakens to his song? When the Acropolis is burning and at the dawn of some new life. . . .'

And at the dawn of some new life. . . . And at the dawn of some new life. . . . And at the dawn of some new life. . . .

Conscious of the curious, even admiring, glances directed at me, I stepped on to the stage of the 'dispatches hall' and triumphantly threw down on the table my bundle of new poems. Then I walked to the front of the stage and began to recite by heart. When I reached the line upon which I had placed such hopes,

'And so the tardy dawn awoke us once again in long embrace—' my voice sang like a 'cello. But I need not have tried so hard – she was not in the hall, she had not come to hear my reading.

'Alas,' my friend, the poet E. said to me in the wings, 'While you were floating around the provinces like a fallen leaf, recruiting village correspondents and fighting the bands, your best beloved gave you the go-by. She is now having a good time with the notorious Petka Solovyov, who used to be so smart but is now quietly employed in the provincial transport department, toiling to restore the city transport.'

A small bubble of saliva appeared in the gap left by my friend's missing tooth and he recited to me a not quite printable epigram about my unsuccessful love affair.

That very day I saw her on the Feldman Boulevard opposite the Red Seamen's Club. She was walking arm in arm with the lanky Petka Solovyov, whom I knew mainly from hearsay as one of the best tennis players at the Richelieu Gymnasium. I had also seen him once or twice at the courts – and what a dandy he was – with a gold badge shaped like a tennis racket attached to the second button of his herringbone jacket. During the war he had been a very smart and dashing artillery officer. Now he went about in a Tolstoy blouse and wooden-soled sandals, holding the arm of my former love and leaning over her tenderly. She was carrying a bundle of textbooks and smiling merrily, looking up at him with her dark almond eyes with moonlight shimmering mysteriously in their depths. I overtook them.

'Hullo.'

'Hullo,' Petka replied, recognizing me, and smartly raised his hand to his old, badgeless artillery cap.

She looked round at me and her face continued to shine with happiness and love.

'Greetings and fraternity, citizeness!' I said, raising my hand in salute. 'Your heart is fickle, I see.'

Her eyes narrowed and she frowned with a capricious toss of her chin, and then, quite suddenly, she slyly put out the tip of her tongue at me, as much as to say – you're too late! And at that moment I realized who she was.

She was that little girl in a sailor's blouse who had run down the gravel path past Bunin and myself at the Kovalevsky villa and several years later had been with that detachment of sailors who had tried to enter the house in Knyazheskaya Street, and now she was studying at the Party School. She was the same woman whom many years ahead

I was to encounter fleetingly at various moments of my life, first middle-aged, then elderly, and finally quite old – among the shimmering antlers of the 40-degrees-below-zero Urals winter and the varicoloured columns of smoke climbing like sheep out of a whole forest of Magnitogorsk chimneys.

She turned away from me, pressed her curly head into Petka Solovyov's shoulder and, having turned the corner, where there stood a huge street poster by Fazini in the style of Matisse – two revolutionary sailors in bell-bottomed trousers with Mauser pistols at their belts against the background of a dark-blue sea strewn with battle cruisers that looked like flat-irons – they entered the United Consumers' Society's canteen in all probability to have a meal on their ration cards, in other words, to eat a square slab of dry barley porridge sprinkled with a few drops of greenish machine oil and drink a mug of carrot tea with two boiled sweets.

Searing passion, jealousy and longing instantly pierced my soul, but just as quickly left it again, giving way to other passions, to another love.

I lost sight of her without even discovering her name.

As for Petka Solovyov, being an officer, he became involved in a counter-revolutionary plot and I read his name in a list of those who had been shot that was pasted up on a hoarding. He may well have been the subject of the couplet composed by some prison wag to the tune of a sentimental Vertinsky song that was rather popular in those days, 'Three young pages quitted forever their native shore.'
'Three prisoners from gaol were departing: an SR, a captain and a stock exchange man. With tears their eyes had been smarting, for somewhere a lorry's engine ran.'

(In those days the shooting was done in a garage.)

'The first for freedom did rightly hope – the garage was

not for him. He had been trading in government soap, which is not such a very great sin. The second's face wore a secret smile as they hustled him off to camp; currency deals on a modest scale – that was his little ramp. But the third was an officer of captain's rank. He went off to the garage without so much as a sigh. There they gave him a bullet and never a thank for Wrangel and for being a spy. So any desirous of captain's rank, don't pass that garage by.'

But it still tortured me that I did not know her name.

. . . An ant crawling over the flower that has no name crawls on to the finger that I place in its way and that may seem to it a continuation of the flower. Then it crawls up my bare arm, still salty from sea water, penetrates a jungle of hair, feels with its tiny feet my warm, sunburnt epidermis and yet cannot from these minor particulars begin to conceive all my immeasurably huge and complex body, all its secrets, its thousands, millions of nerve endings, its mechanisms of sight and smell, its brain centres, in a word, my whole being as a work of art, as an individual, as something inimitable, like a galaxy – it does not know what I am called, what my name is, and that is torture. For it I am merely an unincarnated Buddha devoid of any purpose in life and any idea.

I crawl up the hairy arm of the vast universe, but I differ from an ant if only because I do not look like a mere symbol on a musical score; because I have imagination, because I can call eternity, eternity and time, time, although I do not know what they are.

I can incarnate any of my ideas in something visual, three-dimensional, in an artistic image, although this is nearly always agonizingly difficult – not because I cannot create an image but because the idea is absent and there is nothing to incarnate.

But what happiness it is when the soul is possessed by

136

an idea, by the passionate desire to incarnate it, to give it a name. . . .

In the end I gave her a name myself: Klavdia Zaremba. Yes, that was it: Klavdia Zaremba. Or Zarembo?

What is it that impels me to write about her, about a woman of whom I have so little knowledge, whom I have perhaps invented? The habit of writing, of making things up, of inventing things? I think not. My soul is continually being influenced from without by millions of perceptible and imperceptible irritants, which suddenly begin to demand with terrible persistence that I should incarnate them in something material and three-dimensional.

Why this persistent urge to paint a picture of a young woman, a heroine of the early years of the Revolution?

In those years Sergei Ingulov accused the young writers of not writing about the Revolution, of passing it over in silence on the grounds that there were no themes, no heroines.

'No, this is not the heroine,' Ingulov wrote in the Kharkov *Kommunist*, 'who should enter the literature of the revolutionary epoch in place of Turgenev's Elena, Goncharov's Verochka, and Chernyshevsky's Vera Pavlovna. She is not characteristic of the epoch but she is a product of the epoch. And so I will tell you about her.' And he told the story of a girl from the Soviet Party School, a young Communist, who had helped the provincial CHEKA[1] to destroy a dangerous counter-revolutionary conspiracy. To uncover this organization the CHEKA had to infiltrate it. The organization was led by a young staff captain of Wrangel's army. He was the man to start on, but this was very difficult. The captain was extremely cautious, held himself aloof and within his own organization was connected only with the few officers he himself had recruited. He proved too weak, how-

[1] Contraction of the words 'Chrezvychaynaya Kommissiya'—Extraordinary Commission for combating counter-revolution.

137

ever, to resist his desire to make the acquaintance of a girl he had met several days in succession in the street and in the United Consumers' Society canteen. Eventually he yielded and made her acquaintance. She did not know who he was. He did not know who she was. At the CHEKA they explained to her who she had met and ordered her to make him fall in love with her. The assignment was generously carried out; she not only made him fall in love with her, but fell in love with him herself and did not conceal the fact from the head of the CHEKA Secret Operations Department, who extracted a promise from her that, come what may, she would go through with the assignment. The girl urged them to hurry. She told them she could bear this torture no longer. But the work of destroying the conspiracy dragged on because it was not just the top of the organization that had to be taken but all its ramifications as well. She staunchly performed her revolutionary duty and did not let her lover out of her sight right up to the moment when they were arrested together, locked in adjoining cells, and began tapping messages to each other and passing notes. Then he was shot and she was released.

'Writers of both sexes,' Ingulov boomed, 'tragedians and poets, acmeists and neoclassicists – who are you telling us about? You are artists, you cannot close your eyes to the revolutionary life, to the life – not of classes, groups, strata – but of individuals in the Revolution. . . .'

'Poets and poetesses, you were able to sing the love of Dante and Beatrice. Is it beyond your powers to comprehend the love of this tsarist officer and the girl from the Party School?'

'Why do you remain silent?'

As though it were now, I can see before me the angry face of my senior comrade and friend Sergei Ingulov – healthy, the colour of raw meat, with a cleft chin like a tomato. A pince-nez with thick rimless lenses, the rather humorously compressed lips of the provincial feature-writer inclined to imitate Arkadi Averchenko; yet at the same time it was the strong-willed sometimes even menacingly ruthless face of a Bolshevik underground worker, a true Leninist, scorched by the flames of those unforgettable years.

But there came a time when even he was not spared by the angel of death, who swooped upon him with a rustle of black silk robes and tore out his ardent soul, leaving somewhere on earth – no one knows where! – the prostrate, lifeless body of a man who never did hear the answer to his question:

'But who was she, this girl from the Party School?'

. . . And what did she endure while she awaited the climax on that sultry July day that blazed like the crimson flower of the bignonia, into which an ominously bumbling wasp was slowly crawling, gently parting with its wings the internal organs of the sun-warmed flower that barred its path into the blind alley from which there was no return.

The whole city – its deserted streets, its granite roadways, the motionless sea, the breathless feathery foliage of the acacias, the dry fountains – all seemed in these dread, sun-struck hours to be contained within the closed crimson blossom – the whole city along with the lighthouse overlooking the harbour and, what was more, that great tall building dominating all the other buildings, where at this hour something was being prepared for the evening.

Klavdia Zaremba did not know exactly how it was done. But she herself was locked in one of the cells of this building and all that went on around her and terribly close to her at once transformed her conjectures into something absolutely authentic.

The flower of the bignonia had yet another name: tekoma.

Klavdia Zaremba knew this building from top to bottom,

all its entrances and back stairways, all its nooks and crannies.

Not so long ago – before the Revolution – it had been the latest investment of a certain joint stock company. It stood in a fine residential street overlooking a park and was famed for its expensive luxury flats of five, six and even eight rooms with every convenience – baths, toilets, gas, lifts, stables and garages in the yard, its flower-beds, round ornamental pond, marble seats, its weeping Japanese trees in the middle of the lawns, its asphalt paths leading from the wicket in the forged iron gates to the staircase entrances of the house, which were lighted in the evening with softly glowing electric lights, and only very rich families lived there.

Now all its entrances and exits were guarded by sentries of the special-duty units – Chinese, Latvians, Russian soldiers of the expeditionary force who had returned from France.

This building towered over the city like an Acropolis, and at night it alone blazed from top to bottom with bright electric light above the dark-enshrouded houses.

Sleepless as conscience, it ruthlessly illuminated the very darkest crannies of the human mind, where there might, perhaps, lurk criminal thoughts engendered by the morality of the old world.

But no less terrible did this house appear in the full glare of summer, at the end of an interminably long July day, when the clocks had by decree been put three hours forward, so that when it was still only five by the sun, the city clocks said eight in the evening and the curfew came into force, after which any appearance in the street without a special pass was punishable by shooting on the spot.

The dazzling sun was still poised high over the rooftops but the city was already ominously deserted. Reflections from the windows shimmered fiercely and obliquely on the empty pavements. Sometimes a solitary patrol tramped down the street and the houses trembled as an army lorry rumbled past the locked gates.

What does she recall of those days?

The wall of an empty room with a huge, luxurious desk, on the blue baize top of which lay a Mauser pistol in a wooden holster; a leather sofa and above it, written straight on the expensive study wallpaper in gold paint with vigorous strokes of a broad brush, the words 'Death to the counter-revolution.'

This was the office of the head of the secret-operations section, from the Venetian window of which there could be seen above the tree tops of the Alexander Park with its decapitated column a strip of cubist-blue, utterly decivilized sea without a single sail or a single wisp of smoke on the horizon.

Many years later, on meeting the man who had then been sitting at that desk, she reminded him of that golden inscription on the wallpaper, but he only stared at her in astonishment.

'There was never anything of the kind, my dear. You must have mixed things up.'

'I tell you there was. I can see it as if it were now.'

He frowned.

'You must have imagined it.'

'I swear there was.'

'Well, one of us must be crazy.'

'It must be you, then.'

But a great deal more time passed – ahead – and they met in the central polyclinic outside the consulting room of the head dental surgeon in front of a massive ash door with a polished brass knob, among the square synthetic marble columns and the decorative plants in their china pots on the warm window-sill of an enormous window, from which there was a view over the dilapidated mansions of Sivtsev Vrazhek

Street and the soft blue outline of a tall building with little towers, obelisks and a rather squat spire.

'Hullo, Vikenti.'

'Hullo, Comrade Zaremba. Have you noticed we meet once every seventeen years? Are you fully and completely?'

'Yes.'

'So am I. They've even given me a pension. I am a special pensioner. So there you are. . . . I'm having a new plate made.'

'So am I. I've lost more than half my teeth.'

'You've put on quite a bit. How much do you run to now? About seventy kilos?'

'Why go into details?'

'And you used to be such a frail young thing, a poet's dream.'

'I was never frail. Slim but firm. And I still maintain that you used to have "Death to the counter-revolution" written on your wallpaper. Say what you like.'

'And you're quite right, you know,' he laughed. 'I remembered afterwards and I was going to ring you up about it, but out there, just imagine, we didn't even have a public call box.'

'How funny!'

'Oh, well. . . . How d'you think it happened? Our section was getting ready for the May Day demonstration and we had to write some suitable slogan on our banner. So we stretched the red cotton across the wall and the Angel of Death – you remember him, our Kolya Beryozovsky, alias Angel of Death, don't you? – good-looking chap and handy with a brush too – may he rest in peace – well, he took a great big brush and wrote in gold paint: "Death to the counter-revolution." The paint went through the cloth and left an imprint on the wallpaper.'

'There, you see. And you would argue.'

'Sorry, pet. Yes, you were a great help to us then. I remember how you suffered!. . .'

They scanned each other, remembering themselves as they

142

had been in those days. He somewhat hazily recalled her in his office, quite young, in a brand-new captured British field jacket with her hair cut short like a boy's, thin from hunger, her rather sunken eyes riveted on the golden inscription above the leather sofa. And she recalled him, a rather fussy little man of about thirty with the looks of a small artisan, which was just what he had been before the Revolution – a typical Russian unsuccessful provincial tailor in a cotton print shirt and waistcoat with a blue metal buckle at the back and a fiercely cheerful expression on his snub-nosed plebeian face, now ravished with hatred of the class enemies whom he had sworn to destroy to a man, to wipe off the face of the earth mercilessly, pitilessly, tirelessly. His dark monotone cherry-shaped eyes watched the person he was talking to attentively, almost considerately, so that one might have gained the impression that he was a kindly, perhaps even soft-hearted man. But no impression could have been more mistaken : he was merciless, incorruptible and inflexibly true to his principles.

Since childhood he had suffered hardship, injustice and humiliation, first from his beast of a master, and then from his customers, the infantry officers of a remote garrison, whom he could never please, who often failed to pay him for his work, who demanded endless alterations, adjustments and recuttings, who struck him in the face and had him thrown out of the officers' club when he came there with his swollen cheek tied up in a coloured handkerchief and a blue-black bruise under his bloodshot eye, and he hated them so much that the blood drummed deafeningly in his temples and his breath came in gasps, and he was ready to destroy them all, no matter how many the world possessed, to exterminate them day and night, methodically and in cold-blooded frenzy, and to go on doing so until Justice reigned triumphant throughout the globe and Labour was Master of the World.

That day there was spread out on the desk before him a water-colour diagram of the counter-revolutionary officers' organization with all its ramifications and connecting links, and each member of that criminal organization was shown with a symbol – a circle, a triangle, a diamond or a square with the conspirator's name in it, and in the centre in a green triangle Zaremba read the name of her beloved, upon whom all the threads of the conspiracy converged.

He interrogated her just for form's sake, fussing about and trying to play the hospitable host.

'I'll just go out for some hot water and we'll have some tea. . . . Take a sweet, a biscuit. You must be hungry. You've done us a real good turn – thanks for that in the name of the Revolution. And don't upset yourself over it. Wipe your cheeks. Here's a handkerchief. Believe me, that captain of yours isn't worth crying over, the scoundrel. If they had got the upper hand, they'd have strung us all up on the lamp-posts and the railway bridges – you as well, in spite of everything – be sure of that. It's them or us. Drink your tea. Stick it out till tomorrow. We'll liquidate the lot today. Tomorrow you'll be able to go back to work as if nothing had happened.'

That evening she heard from her cell how they were brought in from the gaol in a lorry and marched off somewhere one at a time, and a little while later she heard a clatter of boots in the corridor and sounds of struggling, laboured breathing and shouts. She pressed her face to the tiny grill in the door and saw part of the gloomy corridor, with its cheap thin wallpaper and fly-blown electric bulb, hanging from a thick twisted flex, which had just begun to glow faintly, casting a phantasmal red light over everything. Guards were coming down the corridor, dragging, pushing and wrestling with a huge, raw-boned, long-nosed fellow with sweat streaming down his pock-marked face and long ape-like arms, a low concave forehead and a degenerate bulge at the back of his head, a well-known bandit and hold-up man who had killed whole families with an axe, not even sparing the old folk and the little children, and who was in addition the voluntary executioner for Denikin's counter-intelligence, who had personally hung several dozen worker Communists from the footbridge at the Main Odessa Station. His name was Ukhov. Now they were dragging him out of his cell to put an end to him and he was struggling frantically and sobbing with terror, half fainting and then making desperate attempts to break loose, run away and hide himself – even under a bench – and kept wetting the stub of a pencil between his thick blubbering lips and trying to write his name Ukhov on the wallpaper as large and clear as he could. They dragged him along but he went on writing and tearing the wallpaper, again and again – Ukhov, Ukhov, Ukhov, Ukhov – until finally they picked him up and carried him away and the pencil tore a last jagged furrow across the wallpaper and broke. . . .

Zaremba wanted to have one last look at Petya Solovyov, but they were all rushed along the corridor so quickly to be photographed that she missed him, and then she lay down in the corner of the cell she was sharing with several others and lost consciousness, and this state passed into a strange, almost lethargic sleep that lasted several days, and when she awoke she found herself lying in a white hospital bed and had great difficulty in remembering what had happened to her.

For about two years after that she was given treatment and taken to various sanatoriums and eventually she recovered.

Several times we ran into each other, sometimes recognizing each other, sometimes not; we would pass by in silence or exchange a few words, and then in her changed ageing face I would recognize the features of that little girl in the sailor's blouse or the girl from the Soviet Party School with whom I had so passionately and so briefly fallen in love.

One day I met her on the marble staircase of a polyclinic; she was breathing heavily as she came down the steps. Her figure had billowed, she was almost grey, her legs had thickened and she was wearing tight high-heeled shoes that obviously caused her suffering.

'Hullo, boy,' she said sadly. 'How are you getting on? You a grandad now? And I'm a grandma. Do you ever remember our young days? All right, toddle on, old chap.'

How many times have I taken up the pen to follow the advice of my friend and senior comrade, the late Sergei Ingulov, and write a novel about the girl from the Soviet Party School. Perhaps this was the only real subject, the rough diamond that it would have been worth while to cut and polish without grudging time or energy until it became a sparkling brilliant. But each time I realized that I lacked the strength. The subject was many times higher than I and it could not be treated in the old conventional way, to which it simply would not respond.

The girl from the Soviet Party School had to be described in some quite new way, something right out of the ordinary, and, as Osip Mandelstam would have said, 'fit to burst the aorta.' And I was still not ready for that.

'What a pity that we have not had time to write our *Revolutionary Catechism of Art*,' Edmond Goncourt exclaimed regretfully.

And how badly I, who had not yet discovered *mauvisme*, felt the lack of that catechism.

'. . . For the whole 300 pages to ride roughshod over all the hallowed opinions, the centuries of admiration, the academic programmes of the professors of aesthetics, all this old artistic faith, which is even more lacking in critical spirit than is religious faith. . . .'

No, no, comrades, calm yourselves, I did not write that – it was Goncourt!

'Intellectual flouting of the general opinion : the rarest

audacity I have ever encountered, and only if one possesses this gift can one create original works. . . .'

Putting it more briefly, one had to be not a Bunin but, at least, a Mayakovsky.

'. . . I am looking . . . for something different from a novel. Absence of plot is not enough for me. I want the very structure to be different, I want it to be a book of the memoirs of one person written by someone else. . . . To be sure, the word "novel" no longer defines the books we are writing. I should like to give them a different name.'

. . . If it is not memoirs and not a novel, then what is it that I am writing now? Excerpts, reminiscences, fragments, thoughts, themes, essays, articles, quotations. . . .

But even so it is beyond my power to fill with these wretched scraps of my own and other people's memory that immeasurable and eternal gulf of time and space on the brink of which I toss and turn until dawn, tormented, torn to pieces by distressing thoughts.

Sometimes I appear to myself to be like the happy tsar who all of a sudden, for no apparent reason, began to suffer from insomnia.

The tale of the pillow.

For some time the tsar had lost all ability to sleep. Even the best doctors and magicians were unable to cure him of this mortal disease. Not a single sleeping draught was any use. Day and night he tossed and turned on his bed with open eyes and his brain was exhausted by the perpetual, ceaseless, unending work of his imagination. He was dying. There seemed to be nothing that could save him. But very late one night, when the angel of death was hovering low over his head, the youngest and loveliest of the tsar's wives, the one he loved best, wearing the flimsiest of pantaloons made of some semi-transparent flowered material, tiptoed secretly into his bedroom, touched the head of the tsar's bed with her slim, tender fingers and said :

147

'My dear, I think I know the cause of your illness. Could you answer me just one question: have you been sleeping on that pillow for long?'

'Yes, a long time.'

'When was it last restuffed and packed with fresh down?'

'Comparatively recently.'

'And, of course, it was your first, your principal wife who did it?'

'Naturally, according to custom.'

'Now let me tell you this, my dearest. The old woman put too much down in your pillow. I don't want to say anything against her. She did it out of love, to make you more comfortable. But just feel it – she has packed it as hard as stone. How could anyone sleep on it? Just let me take out a little of the down, dear, and you'll forget what insomnia is.'

With skilful hands she ripped open the pillow-case and took out a few handfuls of the precious down, then she puffed up the pillow, the tsar put it under his head, felt as if he were floating in deliciously cool air and fell blissfully asleep, and his youngest wife shooed the angel of death out of the window with a towel and, having kissed her beloved lord, slipped away as silently as she had come.

But the tale does not end there.

The tsar began falling asleep as soon as he went to bed, and he would sleep long and sweetly till late in the morning, when they brought him his coffee and milk. At first he enjoyed this very much, but as time went on he noticed that he had stopped thinking before he went to sleep about the affairs of his realm and had even grown a little stupid. So he summoned his young wife and whispered in her ear:

'The old woman did, of course, put too much down in the pillow, true enough, but you – my best beloved! – have made my sleep too light, happy and thoughtless. And for a tsar that will never do. Could you not add just a small handful of down, so that I don't go to sleep at once but have a little while for reflection?'

'With pleasure, my dear,' the youngest wife replied and added to the tsar's pillow one quite small handful of swan's down.

'Now it'll be just right,' said the tsar, and ever after that, every night before he went to sleep he had his most important thoughts.

Naturally these thoughts were not always cheerful ones, but on the other hand they always illuminated his soul with the light of truth.

'Century. The calcareous layer hardens in the blood of a sick sun. Moscow sleeps like a wooden stall and there is no escape from Lord Century. . . . A chemist's raspberries blaze on the snow. . . . Two sleepy apples has Lord Century, and a beautiful mouth of clay. Am I to betray – again that scent of apples in the frost – my wonderful pledge, my vows, big as tears, to the fourth estate?'

The chemist's raspberries blazed on the snow and in an agony of red lights and trucks the face of the capital changed.

. . . 'One: I noticed the banners by the box and the black flute over the desk; I saw the harassed sculptor struggling with clay as he lay by the coffin. Another: The minute, sample of the tested conscience, lasted a century. He was motionless, in an army tunic, as though dictating a slogan from the coffin. And a third: with bags under her eyes, in the middle of the hall, grey-haired and with dry, wrinkled hands, his wife stands motionless, watching over him at the feet of the body like Russia. . . .'

In my sleep, above the sound of dark wings I heard a knock at the door. The knock of fate. I awoke and for a long time could not understand where I was as I slowly floated to the surface from the mysterious depths of dreams that had not yet reached my consciousness.

Before me stood the towering shape of a very tall man in

a felt hat, and I heard words spoken in a familiar voice – a bass baritone – that seemed to *slide down gently on to the lower notes.*

'Are you glad?'

He need not have asked that. Of course, I was glad. But I was surprised he was not at the races, although it was a race day, the 13th of April. He entered the room, which was already touched by the approaching dusk, put his stick in the corner and hung his hat on the knob of the top shelf of the Swedish bookcase, having preliminarily tested it with his fingers to see if it would hold. The last time he had come to see me he had pulled it off and I had been obliged to wedge it in with a piece of paper.

Murmuring half to himself in his rumbling bass, he took off his overcoat and threw it down on the bolster of the sofa.

'Glad that you're glad and glad the *apparat*[1] is glad. It's a grand *apparat*, of which I'm very glad. Both I and my *apparat* are glad. Recognize it?'

'Of course. *The Bath-House?*'

'Do you know how it got there?'

'No.'

'From my childhood. We had bought a camera and the whole family was delighted with it. I expressed it in verse straight away: "Mummy's glad, daddy's glad that we've bought an *apparat*." That was my first poem.' He paused to blow his nose, which was running badly. 'When you write your reminiscences of Mayakovsky, don't forget that fact. It'll come in useful. Or sell it to someone else.'

'Count on me!'

Then he asked the traditional:

'How's it going, *karasi*[2]?'

'Not too bad at all, *merci*,' I replied just as traditionally. This was a couplet from a children's book I had published

[1] The Russian *apparat* may mean any kind of apparatus, from a camera to political machinery.
[2] Literally, crucian, carp.

long ago, *The Radiogiraffe*, and Mayakovsky had taken a liking to it and used it until in our company and, afterwards all over Moscow, it became a kind of joking pass-word.

He would quite often pick up a phrase of someone's and go on repeating it in all sorts of variations, so that the impression was sometimes created that he had invented it himself.

At one time, for instance, he kept repeating over and over again one of Ilf's humorous little verses: 'Marcus Aurelius – who's he? Sounds like a Jew to me!'

Mayakovsky's famous advertising jingle 'Mosselprom[1] is the place to get it from' became proverbial, but another equally popular catch-phrase 'Go where you like but I'm off to the Savings Bank' was made up by Vasya Lebedev-Kumach, although it was also attributed to Mayakovsky.

In general, because he was so well known and popular he was credited with dozens of other people's jokes and *bon mots*, just as all anecdotes and epigrams used to be attributed to Pushkin in his day.

The expression 'The incident is overdone with' – instead of 'over and done with' – I had, for instance, heard before the Revolution. It was invented by a friend of my youth, that well-known wit Argo. The expression was passed on until it finally became the lasting possession of Mayakovsky.

That day he cracked his jokes more from habit than anything else. I felt he was out of spirits, worried, preoccupied, as though he were listening for something all the time. It must be the flu that is getting him down, I thought.

With some disquiet I watched him as he moved about my room, because his arrival was usually accompanied by a brief orgy of destruction, quite harmless but alarmingly energetic.

He would sweep my manuscripts off the desk, push books under the couch, and hide my pens, inkwells and paper

---

[1] Mosselprom stood for the Moscow network of organizations for trading in farm produce.

clips away on the window-sill behind the curtains, as though banishing them to the wings of a theatre.

'Now just remember this,' he would grumble as he did so. 'A writer's desk should be absolutely empty! To hell with all this fiddle-faddle! It distracts you.'

He took a particular dislike to a small dull-silver inkstand in the modern style, which I had inherited from my Poltava uncle, once an important figure in the local *zemstvo*. I kept the inkstand only out of respect for my uncle's memory.

With the skill of a conjuror Mayakovsky would dispose of every component of this jubilee inkstand – the candleless candle-sticks, the paper-knife, the blotter without any blotting paper, the two empty inkwells with their tops shaped like little silver bells, and the match-box holder – anywhere that was out of sight, in the bookcase, under the armchairs, even in the empty Dutch stove, if it was summertime.

As he performed all these amusing atrocities he would boom some lines from Khlebnikov.

I believe this hurried clearing of the table of all unnecessary objects was probably the habit of the dedicated card-player, anxious not to waste precious time preparing the green sward for an all-night battle.

This time, however, he merely gave the inkstand a look full of undisguised contempt and, having moved aside a light silver candle-stick, seated himself sideways on the corner of the green baize-covered desk and in this half-sitting, half-standing attitude replied to my inquiring glance.

'No reason. I just came. Are you surprised? You shouldn't be. Just wanted to be with someone, as a guest. Would you like to have a "free, unfettered talk"?'

Whereupon he plunged into a long silence, deeply submerged in his own thoughts.

His Ukrainian, dark-brown, rather feminine eyes – handsome and attentive – had that from-under look that always made me want to call them 'horned.'

Horned eyes. Foolish. But I always wanted to write it.

Perhaps this is where the essence of *mauvisme* lies – write as you want to write, regardless of anything.

From the corner of his large well-formed mouth, the mouth of an experienced public speaker and reciter with excellent articulation and easy diction there protruded, as ever, the stub of a thick high-grade cigarette with a cardboard holder, which he was chewing or, to be more exact, grinding with his bluish dentures, while his vigorous lips and powerful boxer's chin moved mechanically back and forth.

In his dark, moderately thick eyebrows, the kind of eyebrows I have noticed mostly in very clever and talented young men, there was also something feminine, and the forehead, powerfully concentrated over the broad bridge of the nose, was cleft by a short vertical furrow, a darkly ingrained triangular notch.

Of late he had for some reason let his hair grow long and it flopped over the middle of his forehead giving him the uncharacteristic appearance of a theological student, quite unlike that image of Mayakovsky, the futurist, innovator and trend-setter which had taken shape in my mind from the very start of our eight years' acquaintanceship, in the early twenties.

Now that he has become a monument it is very difficult to imagine him otherwise than as he appears in Mayakovsky Square, on that not very high pedestal with his seminarian hair. Most of the time, however, except at the very beginning and the very end of his life as a writer, he wore his hair short, sometimes cropped with the clippers, and his head – sometimes, I believe, it was even shaven with a razor – was as clearly defined in shape as an egg. This can be seen from photographs taken at various times, including one of the best likenesses by his friend and associate in LEF, Rodchenko, the artist and photographer, in which the great poet with his shaven head and attentive, agate eyes is sitting without a trace of pose on a plain bent-wood chair

153

in the middle of an empty room resembling a kitchen.

Before me, leaning back with his hands behind him on the desk – the desk at which we, Aseyev, Svetlov, Olesha, Kruchenykh and Mayakovsky, would spend all night battling at rummy and displaying our wit amid clouds of green tobacco smoke, there now stood almost a monument. At any rate, his famous face wore the iron shadows of a sombre April twilight, a cold, damp dusk.

The flu was interfering with his breathing and he often had to blow his nose, the characteristic bulbous tip of which had turned a strawberry red. He was in the habit of carrying about with him a piece of soap in a little box and his own hand-towel and, whenever he blew his nose, he would go to the kitchen and wash his hands over the sink with his own special soap and wipe them on his own special towel. When he took these out of his pocket he would invariably begin to shift other articles from one pocket to another : from the back pocket of his trousers, for instance, he would extract a wad of pale-green twenty-rouble notes, prepared for paying his income tax to the tax-inspector, and transfer it to the side pocket of his jacket, putting in its place a small Mauser pistol which he had taken out of the left-hand trousers pocket along with the soap-box wrapped in a hand-towel. He would then put the soap and towel into the right-hand pocket, from which he pulled out for a second a steel knuckle-duster before quickly pushing it back again, at the same time checking to make sure that his fountain-pen, or as he preferred to call it, rather grandiloquently, his 'styló,' was safe in his breast pocket.

'Here you are, comrades, here's my styló, and you can do the writing yourselves!'

He performed this operation of transferring things from one pocket to another fairly frequently. It was as though the act of fetching out one object set in motion a certain secret mechanism that performed the whole perfect and inevitable cycle with its appearance and disappearance of the various objects and their various clicking and clinking like the movements of the mechanical figures in a shooting gallery, activated by an accurate shot at a small red target.

And the small metal figure of the dead man swung upside down on its axis. . . .

'Kataich,' he said, putting the last article away in his pocket, 'you, for instance, are a southerner. How do you put up with the north? Do you often catch cold?'

'All the time.'

'So do I. I still can't get used to this rotten climate. And they call this April! Some April! I'm dying like a monkey shipped in from the tropics.'

He again blew his nose and with a characteristic gesture, using both hands at once, tucked his shirt under the broad belt of his roomy trousers – close-fitting at the hips and broad in the leg – in the deep back pocket of which he often carried his 'red-skinned passport,' his 'hammered and sickled Soviet passport.'

It was then that a quite simple thought occurred to me, a realization that explained many things in his character, in the peculiarities of his art. In effect, he was a man from another country, a southerner. A stranger in the land. And even now could still not acclimatize himself. 'An overseas ostrich.' Anyway that was what he called himself in his poem *Russia*.

'Here I come, an overseas ostrich. . . . No, I'm not yours, you monster of snow. Bury yourself deeper in feathers, soul, there's another homeland below – the scorched southern life. An island of heat. Oasised in palms. . . . But here, from every floor a guffaw. Every street leers. Frosts drench to the skin. Bristling with the spears of smoke-stacks and fingers, I push on through the years.'

For the first time I realized how hard it was for him to push on through the years.

'All right, then, take me in your ghastly grip. Shave my feathers with the razor of your winds. Let me vanish, a stranger from overseas, in the frenzy of all your Decembers.'

I repeated these lines to myself, and he – their creator, ready at any moment to disappear, a stranger from overseas, pierced and bristling with the spears of smoke-stacks and fingers – looked attentively out of the little window which gave out almost at ground level on to the yard of a coaching inn, one of those tea-houses that were still fairly numerous in those days in the backstreets off Sretenka.

The yard was cluttered with shabby out-dated cabs, and the horses with their heads in nose-bags looked in at the window, exchanging glances with Mayakovsky, apparently sensing that he was well-disposed towards them.

Very slowly, too slowly, it grew dark at that vague hour between the day's end and the beginning of night in one of those poor backstreets, out of earshot of the muffled mill-race murmur of China-like Sretenka with its multitudes of pedestrians, and Mayakovsky and I were alone together in this as yet unlighted room – he a world famous poet, and I, who still had not written *The Girl from the Soviet Party School* – both of us, as it seemed to me then, by no means young – he was thirty-seven and I – heavens, not really? – already thirty-three – my life was over! – all this taken together evoked in me a terrible inescapable feeling of regret, of lost youth, almost of incipient old age, when it is all over and there is nothing more to come or, as we used to put it in our little circle: 'The show's over.'

And ahead, on the twilit wall there was a watery ash-grey shadow of indistinct shape that one could interpret in any way one wished, even as the ashen robes of flying Azrael.

'The day burned out like a white page: a little smoke, a little ash.'

Perhaps this was how, in pre-revolutionary years, some

unacknowledged writer, a wretched imitator of Dostoevsky, had been sitting in his St Petersburg attic, when suddenly there appeared on the threshold a dark figure, in a dark, broad-brimmed hat and woollen scarf, very quiet, indistinct, like a dream – Alexander Blok, come to visit a fellow-writer. For no reason. Just to be with someone. As a guest. In the literary tradition. After all, people do go and visit each other. Surely there is nothing more terrible than having *nowhere* to go. And so on.

In all this there was an intense impression of the traditional way of life of the Russian writer, perhaps even of the succession of the generations, the bitterness of inevitable decay. It was quite natural that I should have imagined Alexander Blok appearing in the doorway.

Mayakovsky loved Blok and considered him perhaps the greatest Russian poet since the time of Pushkin.

He never actually said so. At least, not in so many words. But I felt that this was his opinion.

One day in the early twenties Mayakovsky returned from a trip abroad – I think it was his first trip abroad – returned home, to Moscow, to the Briks' flat in Vodopyany Street (near the Myasnitsky Gate, nearly opposite the Main Post-Office), full of impressions, and he was extremely surprised, in fact, staggered, when on the following day *Izvestia* sent a reporter to interview him. This was regarded as something quite out of the ordinary, simply unprecedented.

In spite of the flourishing New Economic Policy the central Soviet newspapers continued to maintain the austere style of war communism, which ruled out any of the trashiness, the gutter journalism, the sensationalism, characteristic of the bourgeois press. And, of course, there were never any interviews, certainly not with a futurist poet just back from a trip abroad. Apparently, however, times were changing. NEP was on the offensive. And here was the first sign: an *Izvestia* reporter calling on Mayakovsky for an interview.

Tense, gay, exquisitely polite, sparkling with all the

colours of his inimitable humour, Mayakovsky in a Paris pullover, with the narrow strap of a pocket-watch hanging from his lapel – it was the height of fashion to carry a watch in one's breast pocket – with his head shaved – hygienic, modern, constructive and also because: 'Do your hair? Temporarily – not worth the trouble, and permanently – impossible!'[1] – striding about among his half-unpacked luggage that was scattered all over the room, his new foreign shoes treading on boxes and bundles, on a folding gutta-percha basin bath, kicking aside coloured rubber sponges, bottles of Atkin's lavender water and green-striped tins of Palmolive shaving powder, Mayakovsky all at the same time made the *Izvestia* reporter sit down to table, poured him a glass of Napareuli red wine, plied him with huge fresh fancy cakes from Bartels and with the corner of his mouth, showing his bluish teeth, smiled triumphantly at the members of the LEF editorial board who had assembled to mark the occasion of their Editor-in-Chief's return from abroad.

As he passed to and fro, he said: 'What do you think? Just suppose it was not I who had come back from Paris but Blok, would Steklov have sent a reporter to interview him for *Izvestia*?'

I am certain that Alexander Blok was always present in Mayakovsky's soul, worrying him, evoking both his envy and admiration.

Blok was Mayakovsky's conscience.

Once, in a certain editorial office, amid the general noise, the babble, the jokes, Mayakovsky quite suddenly, for no reason, apparently to himself but loud enough for everyone to hear, with the restrained delight of one discovering the music of Blok's poetry for the first time, recited from beginning to end without forgetting a word that magical poem:

'Do you remember? The green water that slept in our

---

[1] A parody of Lermontov's famous lines about falling in love.

sleepy bay when in line ahead they came steaming in, those warships, lean and grey. . . .'

A mysterious gleam came into his eyes.

'Four grey ships . . .' he said and paused. Obviously he was entranced by the simplicty, brevity and magic of those three short syllables: 'four grey ships.' A whole seascape in themselves.

'Four grey ships. And how we wondered, how we longed to ask those sunburnt seamen strolling proudly past.'

As he spoke these words he even took a few paces back and forth, as though for a second he had become a sunburnt French sailor in a beret with a red pompon, and as he finished the poem he rummaged in his pocket and unexpectedly took out a small penknife – or pretended to.

'Should you chance to find on a penknife just a speck of foreign dust, the world is once more an enigma, wrapped in a rose-tinged mist.'

Mayakovsky held out the imaginary penknife and actually blew on it, as though to puff away the dust of distant lands.

I could swear that at that moment he could see before him his 'island of heat, oasised in palms.'

Mayakovsky's great strength lay in his imagination.

'The ocean is a matter of imagination,' he wrote somewhere. 'On any sea the shore is out of sight, on any sea the waves are bigger than necessary for ordinary purposes, on any sea you don't know what is beneath you.

'But only the power to imagine that there is no land to the right as far as the Pole and no land to the left as far as the Pole, and ahead a second, quite new world, and beneath you, perhaps, Atlantis – only that play of imagination is the Atlantic Ocean.'

Brilliantly simple, but this is the very essence of poetry.

The antagonism between literary trends. Is this not just a

fiction? In my view these literary trends simply do not exist. There is only one trend in art: all-conquering genius. Or simply, talent. And imagination.

Lenin called Dostoevsky execrable, but this did not prevent him from signing a decree on the erection of a monument to Dostoevsky.

One day I witnessed a meeting between Mayakovsky and Mandelstam. They did not like each other. At any rate it was considered that they were two opposite poles, completely excluding each other from literature. Their last meeting previous to this must have been before the Revolution, about 1910, in St Petersburg at the 'Stray Dog,' where Mayakovsky had begun reciting some of his verse and Mandelstam had gone up to him and said: 'Mayakovsky, stop this reciting, you're not a Rumanian orchestra.' Mayakovsky was so taken aback he could find no reply, which for him was a very rare occurrence indeed. Now they had met again.

Somewhere near Pushkin's statue, which in those days stood on the Tverskoy Boulevard, in a building that has long since disappeared, there used to be a rather good food shop decorated in the pre-revolutionary style.

Mayakovsky, who was on his way to see some friends, had come into the shop to buy wine and various delicacies. Mayakovsky out shopping was a sight worth watching. He gave the impression of knowing nothing about decimals and only the elementary principles of arithmetic, of which he preferred always the two operations of adding and multiplying.

A shop assistant with patent-leather cuffs – like the ones they used to wear at Chichkin's before the Revolution – stood with respectful embarrassment loading into a large bast hamper everything that Mayakovsky ordered. Occasionally Mayakovsky would pause to ask my advice.

'Now then. What else shall we take, Kataich? Strain

your imagination to the utmost. Smoked sausage? Right, sir. Wrap me another two kilos of "Moskovsky," please. Then we want: six bottles of Abrau Durso, a kilo of caviar, two boxes of chocolate, eight bars of Gold Label, two kilos of smoked sturgeon, four, or better, five, loaves of white bread, one large piece of Gruyère, then some sardines—'

And just at that moment Osip Mandelstam entered the shop. He was small and was wearing someone else's very large overcoat that came down to his ankles. With him was his wife Nadyusha, carrying a shopping bag. They quickly purchased a bottle of Kaberné and 400 grammes of succulent, best-quality ham.

Mayakovsky and Mandelstam saw each other simultaneously and silently shook hands. For a time they stared at one another, Mayakovsky venomously downward, and Mandelstam arrogantly upward, and I realized that Mayakovsky was longing to make some sharp remark and Mandelstam was equally longing to retaliate in a way that would make Mayakovsky wonder whether he was standing on his head or his heels.

I studied Mandelstam's upturned face and decided that his obvious resemblance to a small camel did not really give a true impression of his character and was artistically crude. The best picture of Mandelstam was drawn by Mandelstam himself:

'You and I have far more to fear – yes, you, with the mouth from ear to ear! Oh, what an awful mess we're in, my nutcracker friend with the foolish grin. You could so easily have whistled life by and helped it down with walnut pie. . . . But it seems we just can't win.'

At that moment he himself was a wooden nutcracker with a big closed mouth ready to fall open, as though on hinges, and then crack Mayakovsky like a nut.

After a cool handshake they parted in silence. Mayakovsky watched Mandelstam as he walked proudly away, but suddenly, glancing in my direction with an unusual gleam in his eye, he lifted his arm, as though he were on the stage, and in a voice full of admiration, perhaps even pride said, loud enough for the whole shop to hear, that line from Mandelstam:

'Russia. Lethe. Lorelei.'

Then he turned to me, as much as to say: 'Well? How's that for poetry? Brilliant, eh?'

This was the end of Mandelstam's *The Decembrist.*

'All is confused and there's no one to tell, as the blood slowly cools, all is confused and it's bliss to repeat: Russia, Lethe, Lorelei.'

In relation to the past the future is in the present. In relation to the future the present is in the past. Then where am I myself?

Is there now no permanent place for me in the world?

Or is 'now' the same as 'then'?

'Well,' said Mayakovsky *now*, sitting down on the sofa, 'you're the host. I'm your guest. Entertain me.'

'I? Entertain you?'

'Yes!'

'Run babbling as in spring – unfettered, free?'

'That's it.'

How we liked to show off our wit in those days!

'All right. You tell me something unfettered about Blok. You met him several times, didn't you?'

'Would you like me to? About my one historic meeting with Alexander Blok? Before the Revolution. In Petrograd. Well, I'm at Lilya's name-day party. I don't know what present to give her. So I ask her straight out: what shall I give you? Without a penny in my pocket, of course. Horrors? Suppose – just suppose! – she wants a cake from Gourmet's or orchids from – just imagine! – Eiler's. Ghastly! But what she wanted was a signed copy of Blok.

' "But how can I do that when I don't even know Blok properly? Specially as I'm a futurist and he's a symbolist. Why, he might even kick me downstairs." "That's your business." Well, I was in a tough spot, but if that was what Lilichka wanted. . . . That was that. I staggered downstairs. I'd heard he lived in Ofitserskaya Street. So, off I dashed to Ofitserskaya. Fifth floor. Up the stairs. All in a lather. Out of breath. Here's the door. Knock-knock! It opens. "May I see the poet Alexander Blok?" "What name, sir?" Straight from the shoulder: "Say it's the futurist Mayakovsky." And to myself I'm thinking what you really mean is: kid, ruffian, lout, puppy, street urchin. Here am I, completely unknown except to a few friends and acquaintances, and coming to see Blok! Yes, just picture it, strain your imagination! Alexander Blok. A great poet. The idol of the public. "Over the restaurants in the evening. . . ." "I sent you a black-petalled rose in a glass of sky-gold wine." So I stood there. Waiting. Now he'll come out and kick me downstairs. Oh, well. . . . It's not very high. Only five floors. Nothing to worry about. Still. . . . But he didn't kick me downstairs, after all. At the sound of my voice he came out into the hall. In person. In the flesh. It was the first time I'd seen him at close quarters. Fascinating, really – a live genius. I could even touch him if I wanted to. Alexander Blok. Majestic and cordial. With a touch of world sorrow: "Are you Mayakovsky?" "I am Mayakovsky!" "I appreciate the honour." And then, so impressively: "I knew you would come. I felt it. I have waited for this meeting a long time." And he takes me into his study. A real study, of course, not like yours with a jubilee inkstand from the Poltava *zemstvo*! You know what I mean: books, page proofs. That note from a tragic actress. "Put the roses on the table and the roses had to be put on the table." Do sit down. So I sit down. I don't know what to do with my feet. One of my shoes has a patch. Very awkward. Like sitting on a hedgehog. Now and then I try to say something about the signed copy of his verse. But I can't get a word in. His presence is so overpowering. And the worst of it is I feel he attaches world literary significance to my visit. Supreme historic importance. A meeting of monarchs. Symbolism meets futurism. "We," he says, "are going out, and you are coming in. We are the past, you are the future. Futurism is replacing symbolism. You are our death. I accept in your person the future of the world. And, of course, of Russian literature, although you do throw Pushkin overboard from the steamship of contemporaneity. (How they were all stuck on that steamship of contemporaneity. Even my own mother said: "Why must you have that in, Volodya?" I wouldn't have put my name to it if I'd known.) And there is Marinetti, he says. You, Mayakovsky, have a "special stature." With joy and sorrow I accept your coming. It was preordained. At some moment of destiny the future always appears on the threshold of the past. I am the past. You are the future. You are the vengeance. You and I shall have a long talk." And so on, on the principle of "jabbing with symbolism to smash futurism and conclude with realism."

'(And all this time Lilichka was waiting impatiently at home for that autograph! Imagine what a state I was in? If I didn't get it, I might as well not go home. She had said she wouldn't open the door. And she wouldn't either. I was in a fix. But he went on and on: the music of the world, the world's fate, the fate of Russia. . . .) "Do you agree?" he says. "Isn't that so? If you don't agree, let us argue. The truth is born of argument. Though we are following different paths, I am a profound admirer of your talent. Perhaps even a pupil. Yours and Khlebnikov's. Khlebnikov is a genius. So, to some extent, are you." But here he stretched a point to make it sound good, because later on I found out that one version of his poem, "The day went by as usual in a kind of calm insanity" contained the following lines:

'"Khlebnikov and Mayakovsky have raised the price of their books so high that the shop assistant at Wolf's can't help smiling when he sells them."

'Took a nice sliver off us there! But that line,' Mayakovsky went on, 'never got into print. Rather a pity! Publicity, you know. Though it was an ironic jab in our futurist behinds. Still, that's not the point. Time was rushing by and I still hadn't got Blok's signature! I put up with it for an hour, two hours, then I cracked. Let myself go. Exploded. I interrupted Blok in the most interesting place: "Excuse me, Alexander Alexandrovich. We must finish this talk later. But just now won't you give me a copy of your verse with your own signature in it. It's something I've always longed to have!"

'He smiled remotely. But I could see he was fantastically flattered. He didn't even hide it. "I haven't a single copy left. They are all gone. . . . But for you—" "just a minute, don't put 'to Mayakovsky.' Put 'to Lilya Yuryevna Brik.'" "Oh, is that it?" he asked in unpleasant surprise. "Still," he says, "just as you please, it doesn't matter to me. . . ." And with a haughty expression he signed the title page. And that was all I needed. "My apologies." "But where are you off to?" "I'm in a hurry. Goodbye." And off I went like the wind. Down the stairs. Along the street. One foot here, one on the Nevsky. Fairly splitting my trousers. Up the stairs. Lilichka at the door. "Well? Did you get it?" "Yes!" She was radiant and she let me in.'

I can quite understand Mayakovsky. Lilya Brik was one of the most delightful women I have ever met!

It was nearly dark.

I wanted to put on the light but Mayakovsky stopped me with a commanding gesture.

'Don't. We shall save electricity.'

I slipped out into Sretenka to the 'gastronom' to buy something to eat, but the shelves were empty, the show window was full of dummy hams and red rounds of Dutch cheese and the delicatessen department had a display of ersatz coffee and mountainous piles of some sickening mother-of-pearl substance depressingly marked 'bull's testicles.'

But there was still some champagne to be had, though the amount was restricted.

I came back with a bottle of demi-sec Abrau Durso and put it down on the green baize of the desk.

'Nothing else going, unfortunately.'

Half his face twisted into a smile that spread round his mouth in a characteristically deep fold, making his face with its slanting cheekbones even more sarcastic.

'Didn't you get any pheasants?' he asked in a business-like tone.

'No, no pheasants.'

'Did I ever tell you that story?'

'What story?'

'About the pheasants.'

'No.'

'You've missed a lot. From the days of my hungry youth. I trust you have read my autobiography? It's called *I Myself*. There's a chapter entitled "Kuokkala." It has an epic beginning: "The seven-acquaintance (seven-field) system. Have established seven eating acquaintances. On Sundays I 'eat' Chukovsky, on Monday – Yevreinov and so on." Well now, about Yevreinov. In his day he was an extremely well-known theatre director, snob, theorist, aesthete, creator of the so-called "theatre for yourself." Gentleman, aristocrat, fond of patronizing young geniuses. Even tried to feed them. In those days I was a young genius. One day I went to Yevreinov's to stoke up. Hungry as the devil I was. Could have eaten an ox.

'"Ah, Mayakovsky! Glad to see you. Wipe your feet and come in. You probably won't object to a good supper, I can see that from your face. Geniuses are always underfed. We'll fix all that in a minute. Do you like pheasants?"

'(Oh God, I thought, do I like pheasants! I could do with about a pound and a half of breakfast sausage and lots of white bread and about six good glasses of sweet tea. Pheas-

166

ants! Still, there's no help for it – theatre for yourself.)

'I put on the grand manner and replied casually:

' "Pheasants? Why, yes! I adore them."

' "Splendid."

'With a superb gesture Yevreinov pressed the button of an electric bell and in came a maid in a lace cap.

' "Polya," said Yevreinov languidly, wrapping himself in his silk dressing-gown, "this young and brilliant poet is famished. Go to the kitchen, find out whether there is any pheasant left over from dinner and have some sent up for the young man."

' "Yes, sir."

' "Do sit down, Mayakovsky. In a moment you will be served some cold pheasant. In my opinion, that is one of the most exquisite breakfasts – cold pheasant. Bismarck always ate cold pheasant for breakfast."

'And the old scoundrel pronounced the word "pheasant" in the German manner so appetizingly that it made my mouth look as if it had reins in it, it was watering so much.

' "I see you're a great gourmand," Yevreinov went on, and at that moment the maid reappeared.

' "There is no pheasant left, sir."

' "You see, Mayakovsky, unfortunately there is no pheasant left," Yevreinov declared regretfully, spreading his arms. "Can't be helped. This evening you'll have to go without supper."

'Just imagine that, Kataich, I nearly wept with disappointment. But it didn't matter to him. He just started chatting about Gordon Craig and Maeterlinck. That was what he called "theatre for yourself." '

'Let's drink to that occasion in champagne,' I suggested.

'How many times have I told you never to use that stupid word. Only upstarts and parvenus bellow at the top of their voices: "Champagne!" Any self-respecting person always says "wine." And the rest of the company should realize that if you say "wine" you mean champagne and nothing

167

else. And never shout "Champagne!" in a restaurant either. Tell the waiter quietly, but impressively: "Please, bring me some wine." He'll understand. You can be sure of that. He'll bring you the right thing.'

So as not to evoke one of Mayakovsky's caustic half-smiles – he could not abide any popping of corks, although he fully acknowledged that magical sound recording *'shipénye penístykh bokálov i púnsha plámen' golubói*[1] and *'voshól – i próbka v potolók*[2] – I carefully removed the wire fastening and almost without a sound screwed off the cork of the bottle of Abrau Durso and modestly filled our glasses with the fizzy wine. Mayakovsky merely put his lips to it. Evidently he did not want to drink. In general, he drank very little and had a marked preference for light wines, which testified to his Georgian origin.

'As soon as I set foot in the Caucasus I remembered I was a Georgian.'

He discounted vodka altogether. Only Chekhov's government officials, he said contemptuously, drank vodka.

We both fell into a long silence, each thinking his own thoughts. I don't know what Mayakovsky was thinking about but he seemed all the time to be listening for something, expecting something. As for myself, I was thinking about him, whom for many years I had passionately admired as a poet, considering him equal to Pushkin.

What kind of person actually was he, this man who was sitting thoughtfully but straight-backed in my twilit room on the sofa under the Leningrad bill of my play *The Vanguard* that had been a complete flop?

Gorky once said to me half-jokingly and half-seriously that he, Gorky, was no longer a human being, but an institution. In a way he was right. As for Mayakovsky, despite all his

---

[1] 'The hiss of foaming glasses and the blue flame of the punch-bowl.'
[2] 'He enters – a cork hits the ceiling.' Both are from Pushkin's *Evgeni Onegin*.

enormous socio-political work, and organizational work as well, the work of a poet-leader, an innovator who had created a new Russian poetic language, work that Mayakovsky performed no less indefatigably than Gorky, he could never have been called an institution. He always remained a human being – a great artist, a revolutionary innovator with a very complex, contradictory character and a sensitive, easily wounded soul 'bristling with the spears of smoke-stacks and fingers.'

Not long ago, in this very room, Meyerhold had sat till dawn developing with characteristic enthusiasm and exaggeration a plan for putting Turgenev's *Fathers and Sons* on the screen.

The film was to have begun with a school blackboard on which Bazarov would be drawing a diagram of the human chest – white ribs and, behind them, as if behind bars in a dungeon, a human heart, beating at first steadily and rhythmically as the law of blood circulation demanded, then fluttering and leaping until it suddenly stopped in a last convulsion.

'Bazarov a nihilist? Nonsense!' Meyerhold rattled on in his hoarse voice, throwing back his narrow head with its great mop of hair so far that his long-nosed profile became almost horizontal. 'Bazarov does not die of blood poisoning! Bazarov dies of love. He is killed by his passion for a woman. That's it! A mad passion! Bazarov draws a charcoal circle on his chest round the place where his heart beats. With horror he notices that it is love, passion, desire that makes his heart contract! I have every element of the script worked out, right down to the last frame.'

'Who will act Bazarov?' I asked.

'Okhlopkov,' Meyerhold replied. 'I see Okhlopkov. No one else.' And suddenly, turning towards me a face that was so narrow it seemed to have only two dimensions, he exclaimed: 'No! Not Okhlopkov! Bazarov was a futurist, wasn't he! There is only one real Bazarov who can die of love – Mayakovsky! Particularly as he is also a very good actor. Zina, don't you agree, Mayakovsky is a very good actor in life? He must act Bazarov. He has already appeared in films a number of times. But never under a good director. And anyway – he writes for our theatre. We'll talk him into it. That's decided!'

And at once he began evolving quite a different plan, a plan for a completely new building for his theatre.

'It's going to be an arena theatre. The audience all round. Nearly all round. Three-quarters or four-fifths of the way round. Imagine it, comrades!' Meyerhold grew more and more excited, ruffling up his forest of hair, striding to and fro, now doubling up, now flinging his head back and swinging round. 'On the opening night we'll have *Othello*. The stage completely bare except for a huge carpet stretching right across it in only one colour. Bright crimson. What? Green? You see, Zina thinks it would be better green. She's not quite right, but so much the better. A huge dark-green carpet stretching right across the arena without a single wrinkle, dazzlingly lighted from above by all the floodlights; and in the centre of this carpet – no! Not in the centre, just a little off centre, somewhere near centre – a small. . . .' He made a pause and, screwing up his face in delight, held out his hand, as though holding in his long, Paganini-like fingers something aethereally light, small, magical. 'And in the middle of this brightly lit green. . . .' he opened his fingers, '– something small, something absolutely minute but startlingly visible from the farthest corner of the hall – a lace handkerchief with a small strawberry embroidered on one corner. Nothing else! That is *Othello*. That is the real, the essential Shakespeare. Brilliantly simple, isn't it?'

Brilliant, indeed, I thought, but it's Shakespeare and not Mayakovsky that he wants to put on for the opening of his ultra-modern new arena theatre. But why not Mayakovsky? Could it be that Mayakovsky's hour, the zenith of his fame, had passed or was, at least, passing?

And had not Mayakovsky himself begun to feel this of late?

It was becoming harder and harder for him to push on through the years. This was not at all the Mayakovsky of the early years of the Revolution, the man I had seen once in Kharkov during the Volga famine.

Olesha described this very well:

'Valentin Katayev and I were sitting in a box, waiting with frenzied curiosity for the man the chairman had just announced to appear on the stage. The stage was bare save for the table at which the platform party – various people from the city Party committee, from editorial offices, from the Komsomol leadership – was sitting. A huge empty stage with a backdrop of bare walls and a kind of balcony, perhaps even several balconies. . . .

'Not only Katayev and I – two young poets – were seized with excitement. We did not look round, so we could not say what the rest of the audience felt, but the group sitting at the table – one could sense their scepticism – were, as we could see, staring with their eyes riveted on the wings.

'I was sure we were about to see some theatrical type with red hair, almost a clown. . . . It was possible for us then to have such a conception of Mayakovsky. We knew about the yellow blouse and the literary rumpuses of the past!

'But it was quite a different kind of person who emerged from the wings!

'He certainly astonished everyone by being so tall; he also astonished us with those wonderfully strong and handsome eyes that looked from under his brow. . . . But the man who appeared was on the whole of quite ordinary Soviet appearance, rather tired, in a half-length coat with a sheepskin collar and wearing a sheepskin hat tilted on to the back of his head.'

I, too, remember that evening well – Ingulov in the platform party! Perhaps even Klavdia Zaremba beside him! –

and Mayakovsky so superbly drawn by Olesha. But I don't think Mayakovsky was wearing a half-length sheepskin coat and a sheepskin hat. Not quite. I would put it like this: Mayakovsky was wearing a dark-grey half-length winter coat with a black Astrakhan collar and a hat of the same fur, also black, though not quite a hat but rather a round flattish cap, which was indeed pushed onto the back of his head and left bare all of his forehead and part of his shaven skull.

He came out from the side and, taking one step forward with his left foot, military style, said loudly, as though giving an order:

'Attention!'

This was the first word of his famous *The Left March*:

'Attention! By the left – march! No arguing any more. Public speakers, give it a rest. Comrade Revolver – you have the floor!'

This was his programme piece and he drummed out its firm revolutionary rhythms as though he were pounding nails into the bare boards of the stage.

'Left! Left! Left!'

Then, without even pausing for breath, he recited from beginning to end the whole of his huge anonymous poem 150,000,000, which he had only just written but which was already known to Olesha and me and had staggered us by its sheer frenzy.

'Come to us not from a soft couch of stars, not a god of iron, of fires, that with Mars, Neptune, Vega began, but a god of flesh – a god man!'

Crashing up and down the stage with iron footsteps, he pretended to pull a pistol from his hip pocket and aim it into the hall.

'Gun them! Gun down the cowards! Gun those that run!'

His voice thundered fiercely and he ground out rather than spoke the next few lines:

'The real thing! Dredge out your hearts! With fire, flame, iron, light, burn, blaze, bleed, blast!'

And when he reached the line:

'We'll drive you to death, you romantic world!'

it seemed to Olesha and me that he was looking straight at us with his marvellous, menacing eyes and we even drew back a little into the box, blinking as though the light were too bright.

'Instead of faiths,' Mayakovsky thundered on, 'put electricity, steam in your soul. Instead of beggars, pocket all the riches of the universe!'

And then for the first time we fully understood what is without a doubt the most terrible, ruthless and bloody line in all world revolutionary poetry, which our eyes had somehow passed over on the printed page but which now hit us with its full, unbelievable force, crashed down on us like a collapsing wall.

'Too old – kill him. Skulls for ash-trays!'

This was so terrifying that further on, when Mayakovsky completely changed his style of reading and almost sang in stylized Russian limerick manner the verses about America:

'When the world its quintet of continents grew, it gave her a power truly magical. The whole town turns on a single screw, all electro-dynamical-mechanical,' – we were quite unable to appreciate them. And only when Mayakovsky, utterly exhausted, wiping the sweat off his glistening fore-

173

head with his cap and straining his rumbling, already over-strained voice to the utmost, hurled into the black, silent hall the ending of his heroic poem:

'Blossom then, earth, at threshing and seed-time. This is your bloody Iliad of revolutions, your Odyssey of hungry years!' – did we open our eyes – and even then, not at once – and realize for the first time just what Mayakovsky really was, the scale of his personality.

In the quintessence of his spirit he was a tragic poet and only on that path could he create works of genius.

The theme of eternal, unreciprocated love and of death was always at the heart of his work, and of him as a person. Every poem he wrote was an ordeal of torment, a death followed by the apotheosis of resurrection for a new, just and beautiful, eternally happy, ideal life for all mankind.

In his poem *Vladimir Ilyich Lenin* it was the same. The theme of death culminates in apotheosis:

'Higher, sun! . . . Even Ilyich's death has become one of communism's greatest organizers. Slaves, stand up, unbend back and knee. Army of proletarians, rise, rally your ranks. Hail to the revolution, joyful and swift. This is the only great war ever known to history.'

. . . He longed for the Revolution to be joyful and swift. . . .

One of my favourite Mayakovsky poems, *Good!*, where the Russia of Blok sinks in the tragic glow of the October street bonfires, also ends in an apotheosis of the wonder of life.

And, of course, there is the poem *About That* with its heart-rending romance of a boy who commits suicide.

'Cotton-wool snow. A boy walking on cotton wool. Cotton wool shot with gold – the corniest story ever told. But with the grief that was there you could have stabbed yourself through. Wailed out the gipsiest romance you ever knew.

'The boy walked on gazing at the sunset. A sunset of yellow unsurpassed. Even the snow was yellow when he passed the Tverskoy Gate. Seeing nothing, on he went. Then stopped. Silk clutched steel. For an hour the sunset gazed upon that fallen boyish form, while the crunching snow broke every bone. Why? What for? For whom? The thieving wind searched through his clothes and found the note and called Petrovsky Park up on the phone:
' "Goodbye . . . All over now. . . . No one's to blame. . . ."

'How like me that is!'

When I first heard those confessional lines read by Mayakovsky from the stage at the Polytechnic Museum, standing in front of a chair over which hung his jacket and narrow tie, I at once thought of another Mayakovsky, the author of the poem *I Love*, the street urchin dreaming of a great and everlasting love.

'Love you? Why, sure! It'll cost you a hundred – no more. And I, who had no home, stuck my fists in ragged pockets and roamed on, unkissed.'

For Mayakovsky – and for all other poets, too – time moved in the vertical plane, downwards; and so he wrote his lines. For me it moves in the horizontal plane – forward and sometimes back – and that's why I write lines of verse all in one direction – just as time flows.

One night he and I were walking along the horizontal of the deserted Myasnitskaya – he had called on me in Mylnikov Street and I was seeing him home to Lubyansky (now Serov) Lane, and I asked him if he would one day read me *The Cloud in Trousers*.

He stopped dead, glared at me from under lowered brows

and suddenly shouted at me at the top of his voice, opening his great lion's jaw very wide.

'How utterly tactless!'

I was staggered.

'But why? I'm sorry, but for a long time I've wanted – I've heard you read nearly all your pieces – but never A *Cloud in Trousers*, never—'

He grew even more furious.

'A *Cloud in Trousers*!' he bellowed. 'Why don't you ask me to read *Good!*? Why don't you ask for that?'

I felt the bitterness in his voice.

'What? You think the *Cloud* is better? Well, I think *Good!* is better. *Good!* is my best work. And in any case,' his voice rose again in fury, 'don't you dare ask a poet to read some old, past work of his. There is no worse insult. For every real poet his latest work must be his best. If it's not so good, it means he's finished as a poet. Or at any rate, nearly finished. And to speak of that is fantastically tactless! Get that into your head and keep it there. Fan-tas-tically tactless!'

I realized that I had quite unintentionally touched a sensitive spot:

'I love less, I dare less. And time rams my forehead at the run. This is the most terrible depreciation of all – depreciation of the heart and soul.'

. . . It was still twilight, Mayakovsky glanced at me keenly and smiled with half his face.

'Kataich, I have an impression that you have a date to keep. You ought to be dashing off this minute so as not to be late and you don't like to tell me so.'

'I was young when I met Mayakovsky,' Olesha writes, 'but I could forget, give up any appointment if I knew I could be spending that time with Mayakovsky.'

I loved Mayakovsky no less than Olesha did, and I, too,

was young, but even for his sake I could not break the promise I had made.

He nodded encouragingly.

Leaving Mayakovsky alone in my room I ran out of the house and, having mobilized every kind of transport available, dashed there and back – apologized, postponed, kissed, hugged – and, returning forty minutes later, found him still in the same place by the now dark-blue window.

'I'm sorry,' I said.

He gave me a cheerless smile with one of his cheeks.

'I understand.'

And he explained the situation with his favourite quatrain from *Evgeni Onegin*:

'My days are numbered – that is so; but that my life may still go on, every morning I must know that we shall meet ere day is done.'

At that moment the telephone rang.

There is a certain hour in Moscow when friends start ringing each other up and arranging how to spend the evening. Apparently that hour had come. For some reason we had of late been gathering nearly always at my flat and it had become something like a night club.

No sooner had I lifted the receiver than Mayakovsky strode towards me and with an imperative gesture commanded me to cover it with my hand before answering. I did so.

'Who is it?' Mayakovsky asked.

'I'll find out.'

Then the procedure was as follows: I would ask who was speaking, cover the receiver and tell Mayakovsky the name, and he, after a few moments' thought, would either nod or shake his head; more often he shook his head. Sometimes he would add a phrase such as, 'Let him come,' or 'Oh, to hell with him,' or something much worse, after which I would obediently say into the receiver: 'I'm busy this evening,' or 'Come along.'

That evening all sorts of people telephoned and Mayakovsky sifted the calls with the care of a prospector to obtain those few grains of pure gold who were the people he wanted for company that evening.

It was hard to understand what guided him in his choice. I was surprised that he rejected some of his generally accepted friends in LEF and did so with an expression of what I can only call intense revulsion: 'Let him go to—'

That evening a very famous poet from another camp received the same treatment.

'He needn't come,' Mayakovsky grunted and with a gesture of dismissal turned his back on the telephone.

He had recently joined RAPP[1] and was, of course, already regretting it terribly. He had been hasty. It was a false step. I think he had realized by then that, at bottom, RAPP was as much a piece of nonsense as LEF. A literary posture, and nothing more.

Most of them had no interest whatever in the living Mayakovsky, as a person, as a very complex and contradictory poet, someone as independent and alone as Pushkin. For them, as he had been in the past for the futurists, including LEF, he was a lucky find, a very useful leader, a man with tremendous driving force, behind whose broad back one could sneak without a ticket into the history of Russian literature. This was a paradise for the toadying mediocrities, the energetic young people who brandished their fake Left Front Art and plastered themselves all over Mayakovsky, joining forces to drag him down to their own provincial level, who clung to him as barnacles cling to the keel of an ocean-going ship and slow its progress.

He was desperate. He did not know how to get rid of them, of all these amateurish 'Left-Fronters,' these half-educated

---

[1] RAPP – Russian Association of Proletarian Writers (1925-1932).

and opinionated theorists who squeezed their literary theories out of high-school textbooks for the senior classes. . . .

What monsters there were among them!

There was one average-sized dwarf, a tremendous innovator, formalist and revolutionary in art, who, of course, as time went on turned into the most vulgar kind of well-intentioned pseudo-scholarly conservative pen-pusher with a reputation for being a great connoisseur of literature – a surgeon's assistant masquerading as a Doctor of Medicine.

A poet who had fought tirelessly to liberate humanity from all kinds of spiritual slavery was now himself unwittingly becoming a slave, fettered hand and foot by the prejudices of the so-called literary struggle which he himself only a little while before had publicly described as 'literary face-punching – not in the literal sense of the term, but in the best sense.'

All right, let it be even in the best sense. But even so, it is terrible to think how much priceless spiritual energy he wasted on this nonsense.

Now he seemed quite suddenly, before my very eyes to throw off these fetters and become boundlessly free, as befitted a poet each one of whose poems was worth more than all the literary scandals and trends put together.

A time of great transformation began for him with the return of his inward freedom, of his spiritual release. He no longer felt compelled for the sake of somebody's contrived theory to choke back his own song, to cut out of his poems lines of astonishing force, as had been the case with the famous:

'I want to be understood by my country – but if not, if it's all in vain? Well, I'll pass by far away like the slanting rain.'

For those four lines alone – in my opinion – he deserved

179

a monument, but to please someone or something he had to repent publicly for those four lines, and call them 'a peacock's tail tacked on to one of my lumbering hippopotamus-like poems,'

to which he added:

'In spite of all my tender feelings for the sentimental song (the audience reach for their handkerchiefs), I plucked out those pretty, rain-wet feathers.'

What humiliation he, a master of the art, who knew perfectly well the value of those lines, must have experienced!

What was it that compelled him so unjustly and, above all, quite wrongly to call one of his best lines 'wet'?

And what of the endless humiliations connected with the insulting business of getting the Main Repertoire Committee of those days to pass the comedy *The Bath-House*, in which he fought so brilliantly on two fronts – against the Right opportunists and the Left extremists?

At first everything seemed to be going well.

The reading was in the foyer of the Meyerhold Theatre, which used to stand where the Tchaikovsky Hall is now. Its windows looked out on to the Square of Triumph, now Mayakovsky Square with his statue in it, and in those days there was just a green provincial garden there with the still not quite obsolete electric trams running round it, scattering sparks like clockwork toys, those same Moscow trams of Mayakovsky's young days about which he said so aptly:

'Do you understand tram language?'

And even more aptly:

'. . . I will cover with a thousand kisses the wise old mug of a tram.'

The famous electric clock perched on the tram station roof over the unkempt greenery of the garden could be seen from everywhere. Olesha used to call it the 'lucky dip,' for it was here that most of Moscow's important rendezvous were kept, including Mayakovsky's.

A dusty foyer, particularly uncomfortable-looking in ordinary daylight, with nothing in it to indicate that this was the foyer of the world-famous theatre of an avant-garde director whose every new production was an event, a fight, the talk of the town.

Creaky bent-wood chairs arranged haphazardly round a small bare kitchen table on which stood a bottle of plain tap-water and a slop bowl already full of cigarette butts.

But what people! The flower of the theatrical world, the flower of the artistic intelligentsia.

The writers Mayakovsky brought along with him were: Erdman, Zoshchenko, Babel, Volpin. . . .

And, finally, Meyerhold himself, elegantly casual, with a curly, half-unknotted, narrow, badly worn but obviously Parisian neck-tie, a big-nosed head slung back over his shoulders, and musical hands that moved so strangely that one could have sworn he had not two but at least four, like an Indian god. No, that's not my comparison. That was how Boris Grigoryev painted him, and even as wearing a top-hat, I believe – several hands in white gloves. Or perhaps it wasn't Grigoryev. I don't remember.

I think there were even some of the Art Theatre people there. Spies, so to speak, from the enemy camp. Akis.[1] Markov, probably, Pasha, as we used to call him, with his short bristling black brows, like a samurai's, and an innocently malicious smile. He had for long been secretly pursuing Mayakovsky in the hope of getting him to write a play for the Art Theatre. Mayakovsky on the Art Theatre's stage. That would be a real stroke! A scandal for all Christendom to talk about.

('Ha-ha-ha!' Markov roared, almost choking himself with laughter.)

[1] Short for Academic Theatre.

'But why not, actually? After all, Meyerhold himself comes from the same stable. A former actor at the Art Theatre.' (He had played Treplev, and Shuisky in *Tsar Fyodor*.)

Not long ago, by dint of enormous effort and ingenuity Markov had dragged Mayakovsky along to the Art Theatre to see Bulgakov's *Days of the Turbins*. Mayakovsky had bolted after the third act.

In reply to Markov's question:
'Well, what do you think of it?'
Mayakovsky had said:
'I don't know. I didn't see the tail. So I can't make out what kind of animal this Bulgakov of yours is – a crocodile or a lizard.'

Having as usual taken off his jacket and hung it over the back of a chair, Mayakovsky opened his copy, his 'manuscript,' as Meyerhold insisted on calling it, gave it a slap and, without wasting any precious time on introductions, boomed out:

'*The Bath-House*, a drama in six acts!' and, as he did so, gave us writers a sharp look, perhaps even a wink.

He read splendidly and surprised everyone with his subtle knowledge of the Ukrainian language in imitating Optimistenko. Even he himself was scarcely able to restrain his laughter and with difficulty tucked it away into a fold of the thick horseshoe-like wrinkle round his big mouth, from which there protruded the inevitable Gosbank cigarette with its cardboard holder.

After the reading there was, of course, a discussion, which culminated in us all agreeing with someone's happily expressed thought that at last, thank goodness, a new Molière had appeared among us.

In other words, the reading was a tremendous success and on the way home Mayakovsky was jubilant and kept asking whether there wasn't something lacking in Act Six.

'But what?'

'I don't know. You as the author of the *Cherry Quadrature* should know. Now don't get cross. That was purely out of love.'

'I suppose it was out of love that you put my skit into your high-minded comedy?'

'Yes, and think of the publicity it'll give you! But can't you say what's missing in the sixth act?'

'I don't know.'

'But I do,' Mayakovsky said after a pause. 'There ought to be some sort of intermezzo about the great spirit of our times. Otherwise it's unbalanced. I'll write it tomorrow morning.'

And when I ran into him the next day in Bolshaya Dmitrovka Street, opposite the pawnbroker's, he greeted me with:

'I've just written it. Just what was needed.'

He pulled out of a side pocket a sheet of squared paper folded in four, but without even looking at it or even unfolding it, recited to the beat of his footsteps as he walked down the street his *March of Time*.

'Stride on, my country, faster. The commune is at the gate. Forward, time! Time – forward!'

'What do you think, will Meyerhold like it?'

'He'll be delighted. That's the very essence of our life today. Time, forward! A brilliant title for a novel about the Five-Year Plan.'

'And you shall write it. Why not? A novel about Magnitogorsk. I make you a present of the title – "Time, Forward!"' Mayakovsky said generously, giving me a stern look, as though considering whether I could do it.

Soon, however, to the general surprise, a number of obstacles arose in the path of *The Bath-House*: it was something very much akin to well-organized persecution of Mayakovsky according to all the rules of the art, from pseudo-Marxist articles by one of the most unprincipled of the RAPP critics to a general ban on the subject of *The Bath-House* in all newspapers and the monstrous demands of the Main Repertoire Committee, which nearly every day was arranging discussions of the play in various art councils, groups, sections, plenary meetings, presidiums and conferences, where specially briefed speakers in the name of the Soviet public and the working class accused Mayakovsky of all the mortal sins of literature, almost of writing potboilers.

Matters reached such a pass that at one of the discussions someone actually accused Mayakovsky of great-power chauvinism and poking fun at the Ukrainian people and their language.

I had never yet seen Mayakovsky so confused, so crushed. What had become of his fine stage manner, his murderous wit, his stance of the demi-god slaying his enemies one after the other with unbeatable spontaneous shafts of ridicule?

He, the leading poet of the Revolution, had somehow in a single instant been pulled off his pedestal and reduced to the status of a run-of-the-mill, two-a-penny, utterly undistinguished author, 'manoeuvring his dubious specimen of drama on to the stage.'

Mayakovsky refused to surrender and with failing energy fought for his play in six acts, which now, as I write these lines, has long been considered one of the classics of Soviet literature.

'Look here, Kataich, what do they want of me?' he would ask almost plaintively. 'You write plays too, don't you? Do they slash you like this, too? Is this a general occurrence?'

'Huh!'

I remembered a copy of one of my plays so mutilated with red ink that Stanislavsky had not dared show it to me for several days for fear that I might die of a broken heart.

Mayakovsky took me with him to nearly all the readings. On the way he would usually ask my advice.

'Perhaps I had better not read Optimistenko with a Ukrainian accent? What do you think?'

'That won't help.'

'Anyhow I'll try. So as not to be a great-power chauvinist.' And he tried.

I remember how hard it was for him to read Optimistenko's lines 'without a Ukrainian accent.' He did all he could to make Optimistenko nationless, belonging to no one, an utterly colourless figure with a colourless way of speaking. In this form *The Bath-House*, of course, lost half its power, originality, brilliance and humour.

But what else could he do? Mayakovsky was trying to save his brain-child by any means. But it was no use. This time no one made a fuss about great-power chauvinism, but they did accuse him of 'an attitude of lordly contempt towards the working class.'

Who is this Velosipedkin! Who are these Foskin, Dvoikin, Troikin! Poking fun at the young workers, at Young Communists! And the character of Pobedonosikov seems suspicious. What is the author hinting at? Comrade Martyshkin is quite right when he notes that the characters Mayakovsky has collected here are far from coming up to the requirements of the only correct Marxist theory of the living man. So take that into account, Comrade Mayakovsky, before it's too late, before you slide down into the petit-bourgeois bog!'

'Do you ban the play?'

'No, we shan't ban it.'

'That means you allow it, then?'

'No, we don't allow it.'

'Then what?'

'You must draw the proper conclusions if you don't want to deteriorate from being a fellow-traveller of the left into a fellow-traveller of the right, or something even worse. . . .'

Mayakovsky was striding up and down a kind of plywood kennel among sheets of instructions and yellowing theatre bills, ploughing his way through the heavy strata of to-bacco smoke hanging over the table with its saucers full of cigarette butts, its scribbled over sheets of spoiled newsprint, its gnawed pencil stubs and safety inkwells with their violet ink that reflected a dry metallic gleam. His brisk, awkward movements were watched with stony indifference by the various conference-bleared eyes of that devilish art council of the 1929 pattern that seemed soundlessly but menacingly to be repeating to the rhythm of his long strides: 'Denigration . . . denigration . . . denigration. . . .'

He was particularly harassed by the chairman himself, who roused Mayakovsky to such fury that one day in the Moscow-Leningrad Red Arrow express, holding a glass of tea by its heavy cupro-nickel handle, with the thick sole of his shoe propped on the brass casing of the hot-water pipe, furiously gnawing a cigarette stub with his side teeth and looking out of the window at the paired telegraph poles as they flashed by – one pole straight, the other turned side-ways, like a pair of tap-dancers – he suddenly began to recite the caustic epigrams he had just composed. One was against the poet S. and ended with a quotation from Krylov: 'And began digging up an oak tree with his snout.' Another con-tained the line: 'But our bard sings on just the same and to rival Byron makes his Russian lame'; while the third was this: 'Crushing my comedy out of shape, at the Repertcom sits Gandurin. Could any of you a nocturne scrape on this cracked and battered bandore?'[1]

He recited these epigrams with his mouth enclosed in the iron horseshoe of a terrible, ruthless smile.

I had seen that iron smile often enough, particularly on the day I introduced him at the editorial office of the Ukrainian satirical paper *Red Pepper* to Bulgakov, whom Mayakovsky considered his ideological enemy.

With unconcealed curiosity Bulgakov examined this live futurist, this member of LEF, this famous revolutionary

[1] Parody of lines from Mayakovsky's own A *Cloud in Trousers*: 'Could you play a nocturne on a flute of rainwater pipes?'

poet; his piercing, frenziedly light-blue eyes scanned Mayakovsky's face and I realized that Bulgakov was dying to
challenge Mayakovsky to a duel of wit.

They both had the reputation of being great wits.

For a time Bulgakov circled cautiously round Mayakovsky,
considering the best place to stick his claws in. Mayakovsky
stood firm and immovable as a rock. Finally, Bulgakov shook
his blond student-like locks and took the plunge.

'I hear you have inexhaustible imagination, Vladimir
Vladimirovich. Could you help me with a little advice? At
the moment I happen to be writing a short satire and I'm
absolutely stuck for the name of one of the characters. It
must strike a professorial note.'

And almost before Bulgakov had finished speaking Mayakovsky replied instantly, without a moment's hesitation, in
his rich baritone:

'Timerzyayev!'[1]

'I surrender!' Bulgakov exclaimed with malicious admiration and raised his hands.

Mayakovsky smiled graciously.

Actually Bulgakov called his professor: Persikov.

From what people remember about Mayakovsky. Odd
scraps.

'Volodya, you have quite given up learning French!'

'Sh! Lilichka, don't frighten it away. It's ripening by itself
in my mouth, like a wheat-ear.'

'How many acts ought there to be in a play?'

'Five at the most.'

'I shall have six.'

[1] Mayakovsky combined the name of the famous Russian scientist
Timiryazev with the word 'merzavets' — 'scoundrel'.

At the end of a party:

'I say, Olesha has started talking French! It's time to go home.'

'At first you love everyone and everyone loves you. And everything goes well. Then everybody loves you except one, the very one that you love. And it's always like that.'

'I think I'll chuck everything and start reading my poems on the quiet, at a rouble a line.'

'Kolya is a star of the first magnitude.'
'That's right. First magnitude, fourteenth degree.'

'What would you like to have more than anything else in the world?'
'A dwarf hippopotamus, tame enough to sit under the table like a dog.'
'Are there any?'
'I saw some in America with my own eyes, 6,000 dollars apiece.'

. . . And here he is again before me, now sitting, now standing up and walking, now turning round in the completely dark room with its dark-blue windows – an incarnated metaphor from *A Cloud in Trousers*.

'No one would know me now: a sinewy colossus that groans and writhes. What does it want, this colossus? It wants much, very much! After all, for yourself, it makes no difference that you're bronze and your heart's a lump of iron. . . . So, huge though I am, I lean on the window and melt the pane with my forehead. . . .'

And so forth.

He stood listening. Waited. Uttered one of the phrases that used to be current in our circle:
'Charlie is expecting guests and the guests haven't come.'
But just at that moment there was a ring at the bell. A

murmur of voices. The light flashed on. Exclamations. Everything changed. Another ring. More exclamations. And the
guests Mayakovsky had chosen began to roll up.

And what followed? Just an ordinary Moscow party.
People had just 'seen your light and dropped in.' We sat in
the dining room. Tea, biscuits. About three bottles of
Riesling. As something quite out of the ordinary – a box
of chocolates with a white paper frill all round, and in the
middle, one small long-necked bottle of chocolate liqueur.
As an impromptu offering, an amusing curiosity, there were
the left-overs from dinner – a bowl of meat dumplings which
stressed even more the completely extempore, unpremedi-
tated nature of the gathering. We all sat crowded together
round the table. There were not enough chairs, of course.
Mayakovsky and I shared a big linen basket covered with
a brown bearskin.

Mayakovsky rested his elbow on the huge heavy head of
the bear, occasionally lifting it by its black nose and looking
tenderly into its brown glass eyes and the narrow painted
jaws with small, white front teeth and yellow fangs.
Not a bit like the usual Mayakovsky; nothing of the enter-
tainer, the ringleader, about him. Subdued. Gentle. Homely.
'Vladimir Vladimirovich, would you like some dumplings?'
'Thank you.'
'Yes, thank you, or no, thank you?'
What a firework display of quips, jests and puns Mayakovsky would have exploded into at any other time. He never
missed the slightest chance of starting a dazzling verbal
tournament and, of course, emerging from it victorious. In
this field he had no rival. And here was someone offering
him dumplings, just ordinary common-or-garden meat dumplings. What rich material for wit, for verbal swordplay!
But this evening Mayakovsky's place seemed to have been
taken by quite a different person. He answered politely:
'Yes – thank you.'

The man who even at the barber's would command:

'Comb my ears back, please.'

Everyone at the table that evening had a joke to tell except Mayakovsky. The young lions of the Art Theatre kept teasing the famous poet and master of repartee, challenging him to cross swords. They tried their strength not without misgivings. But he either let it pass in silence or made some lacklustre reply. One might have thought he had fallen under the influence of some strange spell that had deprived him of the gift of humour.

On the other hand he shone that evening with a different quality – the precious gift of human warmth, kindness, tenderness, modesty, all the things he usually hid away so shyly in his great burning heart.

The actor Boris Livanov, in those days still one of the bright hopes of the stage, a handsome young man, almost as tall as Mayakovsky, perhaps two fingers shorter, a charming simpleton and *jeune-premier*, who had already tasted the sweet poison of theatrical success, a jester and lively card, was dying to match his wit against Mayakovsky's and went on teasing all the time, tossing him caustic little jokes for bait, but without result; Mayakovsky was lying low. Another guest who would not leave him alone was the young Yanshin, also known all over Moscow for his performance as Lariosik in that most fashionable of plays, Bulgakov's *The Days of the Turbins* – slim, slightly infantile, gently rhythmical, full of a latent, gentle humour that was not, however, without a large dose of sarcasm. He was not a man to take risks with and you had to be on your guard with him; his child-like smile was not to be trusted.

While Livanov's sallies were like iron gauntlets thrown down as a challenge to a tournament, Yanshin attacked more subtly, in a feeble, innocent, clowning voice as though his remarks were just friendly jokes, but they, too, appeared to have no effect. They failed to rouse Mayakovsky from the strange state of trance into which he seemed to be sinking deeper and deeper, only occasionally coming to the surface and looking round, as though in search of something to hold on to.

The human memory possesses the as yet unexplained ability to record all kinds of little things, while the most important events leave barely a trace or perhaps no trace at all, except for some general, indefinable spiritual sensation, a mysterious echo, perhaps. They lie forever submerged in the fathomless depths of memory, like sunken wrecks, encrusted from keel to mast with the fantastic sea-shells of conjecture.

My memory has retained nothing of the most important details of that evening, except for Mayakovsky's big hand, his nervously twitching fingers – they were before my eyes all the time, right at my side – which mechanically plunged into the bearskin and tore it, plucked at it, pulling out tufts of the dry brown fur, while his eyes stared across the table at Nora Polonskaya – his latest infatuation – a very young, delightful, fair-haired girl with dimples on her pink cheeks, in a tight knitted jumper with short sleeves – also pale pink – which made her look more like a young sportswoman, a junior table-tennis champion, than a second-string actress at the Art Theatre.

She was certainly no *tarakutska*, but a girl of the fashionable 'IWW' type, as we used to say, quoting a line from Aseyev.

With a slightly frightened smile she would write on bits of cardboard broken out of the chocolate box answers to Mayakovsky's messages, which he tossed to her across the table from time to time with the gesture of a roulette player, clawing the dusty bearskin with his uncleaned nails while he waited for the reply – 'clawing the den in a twenty-clawed duet,' as he had written in his poem *About That*, which still bleeds to this day.

The little cardboard squares flew across the table over the bowl of dumplings and others flew back. At last the chocolate box was destroyed. Then Mayakovsky and Nora moved to my room. Tearing scraps of paper from anything that came to hand, they continued their rapid correspondence, which was like a silent duel to the death.

He demanded. She would not agree. She demanded – he would not agree. The eternal duel of love.

It was the first time I had seen Mayakovsky in love. Obviously, openly, passionately in love. At any rate, so it seemed to me at the time. Or, perhaps, he was merely sick and not fully in control of himself. Bits of cardboard, scraps of torn messages and furiously crumpled notes were scattered all over the flat. The basket under the desk was full of them.

Some time between two and three in the morning the main characters and the guests – the extras, for whom I have nothing but praise – about ten people all together – began to take their leave.

Mayakovsky hurriedly wound his scarf round his neck, put on his coat, and started looking for his stick and hat, coughing and trying to clear his throat.

'Where are you going?' I asked, almost in fright.

'Home.'

He always had two homes. A room at the Briks' and a room in the big house in Lubyansky Lane, where he worked : a big utilitarian Swedish bureau of yellow wood; a chair; an iron bedstead; on the bare wall a small well-known photograph of Lenin on the platform; the same room where

'I sit with Lenin – a photograph on a white wall.'

I went there once to ask Mayakovsky to contribute to *Red Pepper* and I remember him with his hair close-cropped, gay, aggressive, challenging, full of life and energy; he immediately expressed his readiness to revive old times, to recall the days of *Satirikon*. Standing there beside that Swedish bureau, he stated his terms and promised to come to all the editorial conferences, which he did with the punctuality of a real, professional journalist.

At the very first conference he literally swamped us with new subjects, ideas, fillers, captions, so that the magazine at once began to glow with all the colours of 'Mayakovsky satire,' with his unique and inimitable humour.

Now all this seemed very long ago, a whole eternity, although it was, in fact, not more than six years. As Bunin would have said:

'Six years have passed since then, trickled away as the sand in a ship's hour-glass. . . .'

Outwardly Mayakovsky had changed little. He had scarcely aged at all. But at the same time he was already quite a different person, obviously feeling the burden of life, which every day demanded of him superhuman creative effort, the complete and utter surrender of his whole self to the cause of the Revolution.

In the hall there was the usual muddle, making of dates, the usual confusion of scarfs, hats, coats, and caps; we elbowed each other aside to help the ladies on with their coats. Exclamations. Apologies. Someone was yawning – openly, with all the enjoyment of a real Moscow yawn before daybreak.

I noticed Mayakovsky's congested breathing.

'You're really ill. You must have a fever! Do stay, please! I'll put you up on the sofa.'

'It's not long enough.'

'I'll chop off your feet.'

'And cover me with the Encyclopaedic Dictionary of Enlightenment and put your uncle's *zemstvo* inkstand under my head for a pillow? No. I think I'd better go home. To Gendrikov Street.'

There was an utter weariness in his voice.

'Give my regards to the Briks. Ask Lilya Yuryevna to give you a hot raspberry drink.'

'The Briks are in London,' he muttered grimly and it suddenly came to me in a flash how lonely he must feel of an evening in the empty flat in Gendrikov Street.

'What will you do there all alone?'

'Find some cutlets. I'll rummage round in the kitchen. Our slavewoman always leaves me some cutlets. I like cold cutlets at night.'

I realized that he really was in a bad way.

When saying goodbye, Livanov kissed me in the Moscow fashion. At that moment Mayakovsky was helping Nora on with her coat. As soon as he saw Livanov and me kissing, he inserted himself between us, jealously pushed Livanov aside and, leaning forward, presented to me his long, high-cheekboned face, which in the half-light of the hall seemed huge and black as iron. I had never seen it so near before and had not imagined how frightening it could be at close quarters. He stared into my eyes as if through a magnifying glass – with hurried tenderness and desperation – and I felt on my cheek the bristly touch of his bony unshaven cheek. Then he kissed me with the huge lips of an orator, ill suited to kissing, and said, addressing me for the first time in the familiar, singular form, which struck me as alarmingly strange, for we had never been on such terms before:

'Don't be sad. Goodbye, old man.'

And at once – huge, unwieldy, with his hat pulled down over his eyes and his throat muffled in his scarf – went out after Nora Polonskaya on to the dark, unlighted staircase, where Yanshin was murmuring something in his humorous theatrical voice as he waved a lighted match in the air, which sent something like a shadow flitting across the bare staircase well – the ash-black wings of Azrael.

. . . He was zigzagging at low altitude, circling round the old pyramidal church-towers and repeating the twists and turns of the Moscow main-streets and back-streets, swooping back and forth over the dawning city, rustling the angular folds of his charred robes, holding his two-edged sword poised in front of him.

Very late that morning I was awoken by a second

persistent buzzing of the telephone. The first had failed to rouse me :

'Mayakovsky has just shot himself in his room in Lubyansky Lane.'

He shot himself in the heart with a small pocket Mauser pistol and at once, for him, time began to flow in the other direction, 'all is confused and there's no one to tell, as the blood slowly cools, all is confused and it's bliss to repeat :

'Russia, Lethe, Lorelei.'

With our heads together we sat in the empty, unheated beer-hall in Nikolskaya Street opposite the State Publishers at a sunlit ash-wood table, the yellowness of which intensified the varnish-like reflections of the Zhiguli beer that fell from our glasses, which none of us had even touched, for we were all in the icy grip of bereavement, and talked in low tones of Mayakovsky. We went on talking and talking about him, mustering all our strength of mind and spirit to explain something that was, in essence, so simple, and that to us at the time seemed inexplicable.

'If the Briks had been in Moscow, he would never have done it,' Babel reiterated from time to time in mournful astonishment, raising his eyebrows almost with horror and surveying us – Olesha and me – with his small, childishly round eyes, which were timid and naive, and yet at the same time full of concealed slyness, mischief and a Jewish irony that would at that moment have been out of place.

His round, out-of-date, old-mannish spectacles with very thin rims were perfectly in keeping with the character of his face with its big bald, sloping but uneven forehead with certain concavities over the brows that made his expression even more strained with surprise. A duck's bill of a nose, sliced off right at the tip, and thin smiling lips, shaped like an old Russian letter 'Y', that seemed ready at any moment to open and slowly utter an extremely caustic remark, one of those that he used to call, 'a remark from life.'

'Now listen and I'll tell you a remark from life,' he would usually say. 'Not long ago I was in our native Odessa.' A sarcastically benevolent look from under his spectacles. 'And I went to the market. Yes, our famous market. I hope you haven't forgotten it yet? It's just the same as it was in our day. And there was a tradeswoman sitting with her basket of eggs in front of her, and moaning loud enough for the whole market to hear: "This here cost of living – it'll kill me one day!"'

But now his face is confused, pale; on his cheeks, which are pinker than usual, there are tears.

'Look here, we're all to blame for this. Everyone who really loved him. We ought to have hugged him, kissed him, perhaps, told him we loved him. Just shown him some ordinary human affection. And we didn't do it. We were afraid to be sentimental. We treated him as if he were made of bronze. As though he were already a monument. But he was a human being like anyone else. Always catching cold, the flu.' Nervy. Why, oh, why did you let him go like that, in the middle of the night? Why didn't you keep him at your place?'

'But how could I ever have imagined that. . . .'

'Yes, that's just it! Everyone treated him as if he were made of bronze. But he was a "god of flesh – a god-man." But the real point,' Babel again looked at us, at Olesha and me, with a glance that was either questioning or prophetic. 'The real point is,' he said slowly, 'that Mayakovsky was too much of an idealist. You know the kind of women who surrender themselves too passionately to their love. It's wonderful but it's tragic. It usually kills them because they can't bear the slightest cooling off, which is bound to come when people have known each other for a long time. Life turns out to be too material. Their souls are too tender, too easily hurt. "The boat of love is broken on the humdrum of everyday." That's just what happened in this case. Read his poems again and you'll see. We were completely blind, out of our minds!'

Olesha joined in from time to time. Nodding his great splendid head with its Titus haircut and square chin, which was out of keeping with his small stature, he said:

'Yes, it's quite true. Babel is absolutely right. "She was Mayakovsky's thousands of years. He shot himself here, at the door of his beloved," "Wouldn't it be better to end one's sentence with the full-stop of a bullet?" "A miaowing cat. A smoky night-light. I ring the bell. The chemist's! . . . He hands it over. A skull. 'Poison.' Crossed bones tell the rest. Who's it for? Immortal am I, your unprecedented guest." You see, comrades, he was an unprecedented guest in our world! Remember? ". . . And suddenly I glide round the counter. The ceiling opens all by itself. . . . And soon I am hovering over the house!" ' Olesha looked up with his grey baby-elephant eyes, as though to observe a man hovering over the house. Emotion had, as usual, made his speech slightly blurred.

' "Over the gang of poetic grabbers and sharks," ' said Babel, not listening to Olesha. 'That wasn't written just to create an impression. That was written with blood from the heart. There must be such a gang. Understand?'

'Wait a minute,' Olesha said. 'That's not the strangest thing. The strangest thing, I should say the almost inexplicable thing, though it was completely material, was what I saw yesterday in Gendrikov Street. Until quite recently we used to play cards there until dawn. . . . You know what it was? Mayakovsky's brain. I actually saw it. Almost saw it, that is. Anyway they carried Mayakovsky's brain past me.'

And jumping from one image to another, Olesha related to us what was later to appear with such astonishing artistic accuracy in his book *Not a Day without a Line*.

'. . . suddenly there was heard from his room a loud knocking – very loud, shockingly loud; only wood, it seemed, could have been chopped in this way. They were opening the skull to take out the brain. We listened in horrified silence. Then a man came out of the room in a white coat and boots – either a janitor or a medical assistant, someone who had nothing to do with us; and this man was carrying a basin covered with a white cloth, a little raised in the middle, almost like a pyramid, as though this soldier in boots and white coat was carrying an Easter cheese-cake. In that basin was Mayakovsky's brain. . . .'

The young Olesha, the young Babel, the young I. Relatively young, of course. To ourselves we no longer seemed young. Aseyev had set the example with

'Never shall we reach forty.'

But we were getting near it. And we felt it particularly that day when part of our life had disappeared with Mayakovsky.

'Now we must really love one another,' Babel said, laying his hands on mine and Olesha's shoulders.

And '*he*' was now lying in the right wing of the mansion in Vorovsky (formerly Povarskaya) Street, which is described in Tolstoy's *War and Peace*. The house where the Rostovs used to live.

The hall was narrow. The coffin was narrow and red and – to match Mayakovsky's height – long. Over the coffin stood a narrow black decorative plate. It began just above the top of the coffin and, gradually widening, rose obliquely into nowhere. It had been made by the Left Front artist Lavinsky and it seemed for a second to reveal something infinite and boundless that might at any moment be shut off forever.

The coffin was shallow and stood not very high and the body of the sleeping Mayakovsky in a new foreign suit with the wrist artistically bent, as if those pale fingers had only that moment released the 'styló' from their grasp, could be seen almost entirely, well-built, long, young, with the black hair neatly, unnaturally combed – it had never been neat in life – while at an angle across the frowning forehead ran a fresh iron-blue scar – the result of his fall after he had shot himself in the heart: the target clicked, the mechanism buzzed into action and the room began whirling round along with the Swedish bureau, the iron bedstead and the photograph of Lenin on the white wall, and already there was nothing that could be done to reverse that fatal impulse, or even to turn his head, which was clamped to the floor by the terrible force of gravity, and, as the blood slowly cooled, all was confused . . . confused . . . confused. . . .

The feet jammed against the end of the coffin were shod in big new, very expensive shoes of foreign make with thick soles and steel toe-pieces to prevent the toes from wearing, the object of my envy, of which Mayakovsky had said only two days previously, in that twilit room: 'Everlasting.'

I stood with a black-red band on my sleeve as one of the guard of honour and at the head of the coffin, facing me on the other side of Mayakovsky's prostrate form, I saw his mother, a little old woman, and his sisters in mourning, seated on chairs, their eyes fixed on the sleeping head of their Volodya.

'Hullo! Who's speaking? Mother? Mother! Your son is gloriously ill! Mother! His heart is on fire. Tell his sisters, Lyuda and Olya, that there's no way out for him now.'

Later I saw a high-cheekboned, dark-lipped mulatto face all glistening with tears, which seemed to overshadow everything else. I recognized Pasternak. His hands were moving mechanically as though he wanted to tear open his breast, crush the frame of his chest, or perhaps it only appeared so to me.

There were still not too many people present. The guard of honour changed silently at each corner of the coffin. I don't remember whether there was music. Probably there was. But it could not drown the silence. His readers came up the steps from the yard one by one. Most of them were young people, students, schoolchildren, workers, Red Army men, young men and girls. They walked in single file, their faces, tear-stained, lifeless, past the narrow vases with their long pale, hot-house roses that stood on every step and along the walls of the corridor leading to his coffin.

They filed past, seeing him, perhaps, for the first time in their lives. Among them there was certainly Klavdia Zaremba in an old leather jacket and a red, women's department kerchief, which in those days were already a rarity. She was weeping and wiping her tears with a bent forefinger. She was still young and a moonlit night seemed to gleam in the depths of her narrow mysteriously dark eyes. She recognized me and smiled sadly.

'This is a real blow, isn't it?' she said and, having given my hand a firm, masculine shake, walked out of the hall.

. . . After that she went to work in Mongolia.

But still he lay there on his back, clean-shaven, in an attitude of calm that was quite unnatural to him, and only his frowning forehead with the scar across it spoke of the superhuman intensity with which he had written and what it had cost him to produce his brilliant poems. . . . Actually it was no longer he, but only his fleshly envelope – a magnolia coloured face and neatly combed hair.

'And the nails in his boots looked so frantically fierce they seemed to stick out an inch from those thick soles. . . . He tried to abrase them – but failed! – on the sandpaper kilometres of Nice. On the cobbles of Moscow he flailed them, but still they would not be worn! And when the pain would not cease, he broke down near Myasnitskaya and wept by a street-lamp that burned with the dawn.'

. . . On a boulevard in Sochi a dark round-eyed little boy climbed nimbly up an old magnolia and brought me a mossy-green branch with a huge flower on it. Both the boy and the flower reminded me of Mayakovsky.

'A beacon is turning its red eye. The engine rumbles. Along the shore the Caucasus sleeps late, wrapped in the sheepskin cloak of the mountains. It is an alien sea whose waves beat on the ship. In the cabin is the sleep of death. How sweet the scent of a sick flower, how sad it is! The cloying taste of death is in the mouth. The cabin is a narrow coffin. And death places the final stroke on the dark-blue forehead.'

For long he had existed in some different dimension while I continued to move in time and space, as usual, and one day, thirty years ahead, stepping out of a lift at the top floor in wet mackintoshes, which still seemed to be streaming with the reflections of the coloured lights of Passy, my wife and I found ourselves in front of a brown door. About forty years ago, no doubt, this door had been still quite new, and the warm staircase had had that comforting smell of expensive oil paint, polished wood and well cleaned brass.

I remember a small yellow book on Bunin's desk – Kipling's *The Door of a Hundred Sorrows*, which had then recently appeared in Russian under his editorship. Apparently Bunin had great respect for Kipling, a fact that had at the time surprised me greatly. What could Bunin and Kipling have in common? It even occurred to me then that Bunin was rather making a display of liking Kipling or had undertaken the work of editing merely to earn a little money during his period of semi-emigration. Later I realized that, strange though it may seem, they did have much in common – the same awareness that the age of imperialism had dawned upon the world, an artistic cosmopolitanism combined with an intense feeling of their own national exclusiveness.

. . . I had been on this staircase once before, thirty years ago, when I had visited Paris for a few weeks and, having rushed around in search of Bunin, had ended up in front of this door, an excited young man wearing a smart dark-blue gaberdine raincoat with a silk lining purchased at Adam's in Berlin, a fashionable knitted shirt, and thick woollen tie, but a Soviet cloth cap, which had been with me on the construction sites of Magnitogorsk, tilted slightly over one ear, Mayakovsky style.

I knocked on the door several times but, receiving no reply, was about to give it up, when the door opposite clicked open and I saw the familiar face of Bunin's friend, the artist Nilus, whom I still remembered from 'those days.' It was he who had been living in Odessa in the attic of the Bukovetskys' house in Knyazheskaya Street, and often, when I failed to catch Bunin at home, I would climb the steep stairs to his studio, described in *The Dreams of Chang*, and read him my new stories and poems instead of reading them to Bunin. He had a memorable appearance and I believe it must have been from him that Bunin drew the portrait of the composer in *Ida*.

'Gentlemen,' said the composer, throwing himself on the sofa and allowing his broad, stocky body to sprawl there. 'Gentlemen, for some reason I feel like giving a feast and I want it to be a glorious one. Spread the magic table-cloth for us, my man, and quick about it,' he commanded, turning his broad peasant face with its small narrow eyes towards the waiter. 'You know my kingly ways.'

Or, perhaps, Bunin drew the hero of *Ida* from Ippolitov-Ivanov?

There were no more kingly ways now; there was a shabby short jacket, the lapels of which he held together with a swollen hand at his throat, but the broad, Mongoloid face with its narrow eyes was still there, although it had noticeably aged and lost its former liveliness.

'What can I do for you, monsieur?' he asked in French. 'You are probably looking for Monsieur Bunin. He's not in Paris at the moment.'

'Hullo, Pyotr Alexandrovich,' I said in Russian.

He surveyed me from head to foot, making his Tatar eyes even narrower, but without any surprise, quite simply, as though we had parted only the day before.

'Ivan Alexeyevich is in Grasse in the Maritime Alps, there's no one in the flat. Come in, Valya. I read in the paper you were in Paris. There is no one else at home here either. My wife and daughter are in Grenoble. I'm all alone. Why didn't you come the day before yesterday? You would just have caught him.'

Apparently I was destined never to see him again.

Without exaggeration I can say that it had been the dream of my life to see Bunin just once more.

I spent a few hours in Nilus' untidy flat, where, in such a very Russian way, there stood on the table an ordinary enamel kitchen kettle and a pair of typically Russian pliers for splitting the hard lump sugar, even though the sugar in this case was French and in small, fragile cubes. We drank our tea with little lumps of sugar in our mouths and blowing on our saucers and argued and argued until we were both hoarse.

He shouted that we, in the Soviet Union, had no freedom and I shouted that they, in France, had no freedom. And after that we both with tears of love and affection shouted about Bunin, his brilliance, the impossibility of imitating him, and the fact that he had never been fully appreciated. . . . And after that he began to ask me about Russia and I told him about the gigantic building programme, about the Dnieper Dam, which in its scaffolding looked like a besieged Troy, and about Magnitogorsk, a giant metallurgical complex rising magically out of the desolate Pugachev steppes, where the brown leaning towers of the dunes race along in rapid procession and whirlwinds sweep away tents and carry them up to the clouds like a flock of wild geese. . . .

Paris, of course, was as fascinating as ever, but I missed Mayakovsky. I was living in a hotel that Mayakovsky had once recommended to me. He was no longer on this earth but my notebook contained a short list of the Montparnasse hotels Mayakovsky had dictated to me; among them was the Hotel Raspail, where I had taken up my quarters. Maya-kovsky himself, a devoted 'Montparnassian,' usually stayed not far away, in the Hotel Istrie in the Rue Campagne 1-er, in a small cheap room. He would 'sit' in the bar of La Coupole, where it was always possible to contact him when he was in Paris. On one wall of La Coupole there is a roll of honour of the famous people who have frequented this establishment and it includes Mayakovsky's name. I became a frequenter of La Coupole. Without Mayakovsky the café seemed empty to me. Here, in the mornings I would work on the continuation of my chronicle *Time, Forward!*, which was coming out chapter by chapter in the magazine *Krasnaya Nov*, and the figure of Mayakovsky seemed to stand invisible beside my table. His *March of Time* was thundering over the Soviet land, which had started on the unprecedented feat of labour of the first Five-Year Plans. I was overflowing with the rhythms of socialism in the making and could not tear myself away from my chronicle, so I went on writing and writing wherever I could and on whatever I could; in a notebook, on paper napkins, on cigarette packets. . . .

Magnitogorsk had become for me the city of Mayakovsky and I was longing to meet the first, now almost completed blast furnace, the biggest in the world, which was now striding about its construction site in its unbuttoned iron coat, a head taller than any of the other projects that were advancing amid billows of scorching steppeland dust towards the clouds and the sand hills.

Presently I left for Moscow, in a hurry to give in the current chapters to the magazine, and spent a whole day lolling on the seat of an empty compartment, gorging myself on Bunin's latest poems and stories, all of them new to me. They put me in raptures and at the same time proved somehow depressingly unsatisfying, a fact that I found difficult to admit even to myself. I felt like weeping in despair at the thought of the ghastly tragedy that Bunin had experienced, of the irreparable mistake he had made in leaving his own country. A phrase Nilus had used persisted in my mind:

'But what kind of editions does Ivan have? Five hundred, eight hundred copies.'

'At home he would have been published in hundreds of thousands,' I almost groaned. 'How terrible! A great writer with no readers. Why did he emigrate? What for?'

'For the sake of freedom, of independence,' Nilus said sternly.

I understood: Bunin had given up the two most precious things of all – Country and the Revolution – for the mess of pottage of the so-called freedom and so-called independence he had spent his whole life in seeking; this I realized when after the war, in 1946, I received from him one of the best books he ever wrote, *Lika*, where I read the following passages, which shook me profoundly:

'I would call at the library. It was an old and exceptionally rich library. But how miserable it was, how unwanted by anyone! . . . I used to take out . . . various "Lives of the Great," always to seek some support there for myself, to compare myself enviously with the great. . . . "The Great"! What countless numbers of poets, novelists, story-tellers there had been on this earth, and how many had survived? Always only those same eternal names! Homer, Horace, Virgil, Dante, Petrarch. . . Shakespeare, Byron, Shelley, Goethe. . . Racine, Molière. . . . Always the same *Don Quixote*, the same *Manon Lescaut*. . . . In that room I remember reading Radishchev for the first time – with tremendous admiration. "I looked around me and my soul was envenomed by the sufferings of mankind!" That was language, a cast of soul that I understood.'

'. . . Like a detective I pursued now one, now another passer-by, staring at his back, his galoshes, trying to understand, to catch something within, to get inside him. . . . To write! Yes, roofs, galoshes, backs – these were what one must write about, and certainly not for the sake of fighting tyranny and oppression, defending the downtrodden and dispossessed, producing vivid characters, broad pictures of society, of modern times, its moods and trends!'

'Social contrasts! I thought caustically, ridiculing someone's views, as I walked by amid the dazzle and brilliance of the show windows. . . In Moskovskaya Street I dropped into a coachman's tea-house, sat amid its talk, its cramped steamy warmth and looked at the fleshy scarlet faces, at the red beards, at the rusty, peeling tray on which there stood in front of me two white teapots with wet strings tying their tops to their handles. . . . Observation of the life of the common people? You are mistaken – only of this tray, of this wet string!'

(Ah, that famous Russian tavern. What poet has not been fascinated by its colours! Remember Mayakovsky's 'Fall in love beneath the sky of the taverns with the poppies on the china teapots!')

'. . . Sitting in a sledge,' I read in Bunin, while Belgium's small blast furnaces flashed by the windows, 'plunging and sliding with it from one pothole into another, I raise my head. The night, it seems, is moonlit: a pale face gleams whitely, appearing and disappearing behind the vaguely moving winter clouds. How high it is, how remote from everything! The clouds move on and uncover it, then enclose it again – but what does it care! They are of no consequence! I crane my neck till it hurts, I fix my eyes upon this moon and try to understand, as it suddenly emerges gleaming from behind the clouds, what kind of thing it is. The white mask of a dead man? All radiant from within, but what kind of radiance? Stearin? Yes, stearin! And that's how I shall describe it somewhere!'

That was what he taught me too. 'Describe a sparrow. Describe a girl.' But what had it all come to? I had described a girl, but she had turned out to be a 'girl from the Party School,' a heroine of the Revolution. And it was Mayakovsky who taught me the Revolution. 'Describe Magnitogorsk. Time, forward.' And the girl from the Party School having returned from Mongolia, became the leader of a team of concrete-pourers and scaled the scaffolding of the Coke and Chemical Works in her old leather jacket and red kerchief faded by the sun of the steppes.

Sometimes I again turned into Pcholkin for a time. He was still working on poetry and Pcholkin's verses were not bad, in the spirit of the early, still very raw *mauvisme*.

'Late frosts have sealed the spring with ice, yet the young air is scented with the lemon fragrance of mimosa and I run as I did in winter, breathing on my gloveless hands to where spring's glassy imprint gleams.' – 'It was May and planes could fly all night and in that everlasting light the barrage balloons hung like dead animals in the sky. – For days my soul has been but half alive, yet still my heart beats and the days revolve in double dread – of life that is not life, and yet what strife to stay among the dead. – When it's time for me to die, I'll leave this life without regret. On a simple bed I'll lie and all forgive and all forget. – Have no faith in Caesar's greatness. There is but one bronze door, a little open in the dark, and on the threshold – two silent sentinels – Whether a star dies fast or slow we know not. From afar it's sudden, like a shot – and nothing more to show.'

I had learned to see the world from both of them – Bunin and Mayakovsky. But their two worlds were different.

Bunin thought, and was apparently profoundly convinced, that he was completely independent, a pure artist, a portrayer, who had nothing to do with either 'social contrasts' or with 'fighting against tyranny and oppression, defending the downtrodden and dispossessed,' and, of course, had nothing whatsoever to do with the Revolution, or to be more exact, did not accept it at all, was even hostile to it.

This was merely a childish illusion, an urge to attain an imaginary artistic independence.

If Leo Tolstoy, who utterly rejected any kind of

Revolution, who was deeply estranged from anything of the kind, and considered it to be something absolutely non-moral, had one fine day been told that he was the mirror of the Russian revolution, he would probably have been profoundly indignant, quite sincerely believing that this was nonsense. And yet it is the truth.

Bunin wanted to be perfectly free of any obligations to the society in which he lived, to his country. He believed that, as an emigré, he had achieved his aim. Abroad he appeared to himself to be perfectly free to write anything he felt like writing without having to obey state censorship or the judgement of society. Neither the French state, nor Paris society, nor the Catholic Church was in any way concerned about Bunin. He wrote anything he wanted to write, unrestrained by any moral circumstances or even, sometimes, by the simple considerations of decency. As a portrayer he grew and by the end of his life had achieved the highest degree of plastic perfection. But the absence of any moral pressure from outside meant that Bunin ceased to choose a point of application for his abilities, for his spiritual energies. He was unable to grapple with the 'thousand-headed hydra of empiricism' of which Goethe had spoken, and it swallowed him up, or rather, he was blown to pieces by it, like a deep-water fish that has grown accustomed to a pressure of tens, hundreds, perhaps, thousands of atmospheres and suddenly finds itself on the surface, experiencing practically no pressure at all.

For him artistic creation ceased to be a struggle and became merely a habit of portraying, a gymnastics of the imagination.

I remembered his once saying to me that it was possible to express everything in words, but that there was a certain limit which even the greatest poet could not overcome. There always remained something that 'no words could express' and one must reconcile oneself to the fact. Perhaps this was true. But Bunin set this limit, this governor, for himself too early. At one time it seemed to me that he had reached complete and final perfection in portraying the most profound subtleties of the world around us, of nature. In this respect, of course, he surpassed Polonsky and Fet, but nevertheless – although he himself was not aware of it – he in some respects fell short of Innokenti Annensky, and later, of Pasternak and Mandelstam in their later periods, who managed to add yet another division to the counter of representational skill.

All these thoughts flashed through my mind as we, having rung the bell, stood at Bunin's door. A moment later it clicked open and against a background of a neglected Moscow entrance hall, not at all Parisian and very much old-regime, I saw in front of me Vera Nikolayevna, now a very old lady, tall, awkward, badly dressed, a kindly, helpless, much deteriorated gentlewoman, in big, patched shoes, who had retained something of the manners of an old-time Moscow student from a liberal family. Her once ethereal flaxen hair had long since thinned and turned white as snow, but was still swept back in a scrappy little bun, and her tapered, rather gristly nose with azure veins round the once beautiful blue eyes, and her unwrinkled forehead, still reminded me in some way of a Greek goddess. She was probably in her nineties.

Joyfully and sadly, through tears, she surveyed us, and I actually felt a sense of kinship in her harassed, transparently white, bloodless, kindly face.

'So at last we have met again, Valya,' she said, moving her slightly shaking head from side to side. 'Yes, Ivan Alexeyevich and I imagined your wife just as she is, but we couldn't picture what your children were like. To Ivan Alexeyevich that seemed altogether incredible – Valya Katayev's children! All we knew was that you had a boy and a girl.'

'We acquired a granddaughter not so long ago,' I said not without a touch of pride.

'Goodness me!' Vera Nikolayevna exclaimed, clasping and unclasping her old hands. 'You know, Valya, we haven't seen each other for forty years. Forty years! We didn't even have time to say goodbye.'

'I was down with the typhus.'

'We knew that. Ivan Alexeyevich wanted to visit you in hospital. . . . But you know Ivan Alexeyevich. . . he was so afraid of infection. . . . He was sure you would not live, but I had faith. . . . I prayed for you and believed. . . . And many more times. . . . And many more times. . . . And seeing you again like this, alive and. . . . But don't let's talk about it. . . . It's all so incredible, incredible. . . .' And suddenly in the much younger voice of a society lady she said: 'Do you remember Natasha N.? What a lovely girl she was, wasn't she? And you were so well suited to one another. Ioann and I used to admire you in secret. And later on we often thought about you and spoke of you.'

I have a good memory but, oddly enough, I had very quickly forgotten that lovely girl of sixteen and had never thought of her again, and only now, after what Vera Nikolayevna had said, was I suddenly overwhelmed with memories of moonlit, astonishingly bright nights over a silver sea, a hot midnight breeze hurrying through the silvery bushes of steppe wormwood with its strange unpleasant balsamic scent, and a sprig of jasmine with a yellow centre to every luminous blossom that seemed too vividly white in the moonlight, adorning the aristocratically small brunette head of Natasha, whose rather big mouth and animatedly passionate eyes reminded one of Tolstoy's Natasha Rostova.

Perhaps it was that likeness that had made Bunin remember her – and me as well, as one of a pair?

No doubt she was beautiful but I had forgotten her. The girl who had engraved herself in my memory for life was that little barefooted creature whom Bunin several years earlier at the Kovalevsky villa had commanded me to describe!

'So this is you!' Vera Nikolayevna said to my wife and kissed her on her tear-stained cheek. 'Ivan Alexeyevich was fond of Valya and always remembered him. He knew all about him, read everything he had written and took a pride in his successes. You see, Ivan Alexeyevich was your husband's literary godfather,' she added, eyeing my wife severely, while I looked at Vera Nikolayevna with the same anxious attention with which the young Bunin had once looked at the moon, wishing to describe it as exactly as possible. What was she like? Stearin?

Now I think I have found the definition for that whiteness that dominated Vera Nikolayevna's whole appearance. It was the colour of a white mouse with pinkish eyes.

She took us into the dining room and again I was struck by the neglect, the blackness of the unpolished parquet floor, the awfully pre-revolutionary Russian sideboard with its top burned through in several places, the dinner table covered with Russian oilcloth, also pre-revolutionary, a rusty brown colour with round stains left by glasses and frayed edges, and a badly burned kettle standing on a wire gas-ring, and the different-sized Russian Kuznetsov and French Limoges cups, and among them, a plate of meringues – the only attractive thing on the table.

'Your favourites,' she said, noticing the pleasure with which I was eyeing the meringues.

'How did you know I like meringues?'

'I remember,' she replied sadly. 'One day you said that when you got rich you would buy whipped-cream meringues at Fanconi's every day.'

'Did I really say that?'

'Of course, you did. Ioann roared with laughter over it – how little he needs to make him happy, he said. Don't you remember how you ate nearly all the meringues when you went to tea at Natasha N.'s one day and her gracious *maman* nearly told you never to come again?'

'You even remember that!'

'I remember everything,' she said sadly, moving her shaking head from side to side.

Immediately I pictured her under an umbrella in her old *imperméable* walking in the rain to the Place Muette with its lighted shop windows that gleamed like quicksilver, and going into the confectioner's, where a young mademoiselle in a lace apron, one small pink finger with its well-tended mother-of-pearl nail fastidiously raised, would carefully pick up the fragile whipped cream meringues with a pair of broad silver tongs and pack them side by side, like babies, in a cardboard box.

'Here is the Ivan Alexeyevich that you knew,' she said, taking us into a small room, where on the dark, flimsy wallpaper of one wall there had been arranged a kind of ikonostasis – photographs of Bunin at different periods of his life and among them, 'the Bunin that you knew, the best known pre-revolutionary photograph of him: Iv. Bunin, Academician, at the zenith of his fame, the features I should remember all my life – that haughty face with its stylish, triangular beard and long-sighted, seemingly tear-washed eyes.

Here, too, there was a photograph of another Bunin, one that I had not known – a young Bunin in a black sheepskin cloak and a nobleman's military-style cap, and also the Bunin of later years, without any moustache or beard, his clean-shaven, muscular, aged face, but with the same sharp glance, perhaps even more arrogant and inflexible, that seemed to say, 'No, there can be no return to the past!' – and with the same narrow, goat-like cheeks, which made it impossible not to recognize the former Bunin.

'Just imagine,' Vera Nikolayevna said, observing the expression on my face as I examined Bunin's photograph. 'One fine day he comes back from the barber's without his moustache and beard. I simply gasped! At first I couldn't bear it. There was something actor-like, foreign, naked about it, but I got used to it in the end. But why he had to do it I just don't know. Can you tell me?'

I had seen the photograph of the clean-shaven Bunin many times before and had become accustomed to his new face. For me the old and the new Bunin seemed to have fused into a single whole that differed very little from my usual conception of him. It was still the same man, artist, poet, teacher, a great portrayer of nature, the one who while he was still quite young had written:

'Vot káplya, kak shlyápka gvozdyá upála – i, sótnyami ígol zatóny prudóv borozdyá, sverkáyushchiy liven' zaprýgal.'[1]

The remarkable thing about those lines was that they were later repeated many times in all kinds of different ways by various mediocre prose writers and poets, who were innocently convinced that they, and no one else, had discovered the similarity between a falling raindrop and the top of a nail, never suspecting that the magical force of this image lies not in the visual resemblance, but in the sounds 'plya' and 'shyla', which evoke in the reader's imagination a sound not pronounced by the poet and yet mysteriously present beyond the verbal texture, the sound of that raindrop, reminiscent of the top of a nail, as it splashes on the water of a pond.

Although I must add that old man Nekrasov, long before Bunin, wrote: 'Svétlye, slóvno iz stáli týsyachi mélkikh gvozdéi shlyápkami vniz poskakáli.'[2]

One day, as though wishing to make a complete break with the past, Bunin had his beard and moustache shaven off, fearlessly exposing his senile chin and energetic mouth, and in this new shape, in a tail-coat and with a starched shirt-front over his broad chest, he received from the hands of the King of Sweden the diploma of a Nobel Prize winner, a gold medal and a small portfolio of yellow leather, specially embossed and painted à la Russe, a style that Bunin, incidentally, simply could not stand.

[1] Literally: 'And now a drop, like the top of a nail, has fallen – and with hundreds of needles furrowing the still waters of the ponds the downpour begins to leap.'
[2] Literally: 'Bright, as though made of steel, thousands of tiny nails galloped tops down.'

Vera Nikolayevna also showed us a yellowed French newspaper with a full-length picture on the front page of 'Jean Bounine,' winner of the 'Prix Nobel,' in the same tail-coat with his bare, Catholic chin jutting out, and in all this there was something endlessly bitter, I should even say, cruelly meaningless.

'And it was here, on this couch, that Ivan Alexeyevich died.' Vera Nikolayevna went over to a sagging mattress on legs, covered with a shabby carpet, at the head of which stood an ancient folding ikon in blackened silver, which Bunin took with him everywhere and never parted with. On the wall above hung several other ikons in gilded mountings, as well as baptismal crucifixes and even, I believe, faceted crystal Easter eggs, but all this only served to emphasize the squalid appearance of the couch on which Bunin had died.

'How did it happen?' I asked.

'Ivan Alexeyevich was tremendously healthy and hardly ever fell ill. The doctors used to say he had the chest of a blacksmith. He only suffered from one disease in his life. You know what that was,' said Vera Nikolayevna, addressing me with a little smile as 'one of the family,' of whom there was no need to be shy. 'Piles. But people don't die of that,' she added sadly. 'Ivan Alexeyevich simply died of old age. He was eighty-three. Towards the end he became very weak. We had even to carry him to the bath-room. I didn't want to leave him alone at night, so I slept with him on this couch. I used to roll myself up in a ball at his feet and lie very still, so as not to disturb him.

'On November 7th, the very day when you were celebrating the anniversary of the Revolution, he went to sleep in the evening and slept nearly all night quite peacefully. But all of a sudden, some time between two and three in the morning he jerked as if he had received an electric shock, gave me a great push, and sat up in bed with such an expression of horror on his face that I realized this was the end.

The light from the Passy street-lamps was very dim, but I think that what was left of his grey hair was actually standing on end. He tried to say something, or shout, perhaps. His whole body began to twitch and suddenly his mouth fell open in a strange way. The lower jaw dropped like this—'

With her habitual automatism Vera Nikolayevna imitated Bunin's death agony. Her mouth fell open strangely, her lower jaw dropped and I suddenly saw the face of Bunin as it must have been in his last moment, the mad white eyes of Ioann the Terrible, the skull covered with cold sweat, the black cavern of the open mouth with its sagging jaw.

'And then he fell back on the bed, dead. I tied up his jaw with a napkin, laid out his body while it was still warm, crossed his withered arms on his chest, closed his eyes, pressed my thumb on his eyelids and did not telephone anyone until morning. I spent the rest of the night, our last night together, lying as usual at his feet as they grew cold, on the torn sheet under the threadbare blanket and remembered the agonizingly difficult life we had lived together, our former love, our wanderings, and while I lay alone with him there, I cried and cried until I had cried out all my tears. Since then I have lost the ability to cry. My eyes are dry forever. I have no more tears.'

Quite soon afterwards I heard that Vera Nikolayevna had died and I imagined Passy, the Place Muette, the little Rue Jacques Offenbach, and the temporarily deserted flat, squalid and neglected, with its stagnant smells of dirty bed linen, its unwashed windows and the lights of Paris beyond, its bath-room with darned underclothes hanging on a line and yellow water still trapped at the bottom of the peeling bath, and in the lavatory the thick black waste pipes and the cast-iron tank were oozing with rusty drops of cold water and the wooden seat stood in a damp corner like a yoke, and the tiled floor was slightly slimy, and through the open door of the kitchen one could see a gas-stove with unwashed saucepans covered with yellowed sheets of *Figaro*, while in the corner, tied up

215

with string, stood a pile of author's copies of *Dark Avenues*.

But it was a wonderful French spring, a little rainy, with patches of blue in the turbid, moving sky, with a sunny mist over the slate roofs of the old towns, over the Gothic and Romanesque cathedrals, over the meadows, woods and flowering chestnuts – pink and white – round the châteaux and Norman farms, and we were returning to Paris from a trip along the Channel coast.

That winter I flew to Magnitogorsk, and when I returned to Moscow I received from Magnitogorsk a letter written in an almost illegible and quite unfamiliar hand.

'Why didn't you come and see me, you rascal, when you were here? I have been living in Magnitogorsk for ages with my eldest girl. I look after her little boys for her. I'm on pension now, of course, but as a social service I give lectures at the house committee on the history of the Party. Lately I have been very ill. I have broken my leg and have had to lie up at home, otherwise I would have been out looking for you. Not so long ago they put me in hospital, cut me open and sewed me up again and told me there was nothing wrong and I would soon feel all right again. But I think they're having me on. Very humane of them! I feel I shall soon be packing up altogether. We may never see each other again. So, I confess to you alone before I die: I loved him and did not forget him for one minute all my life. You know who. But my conscience is clear before the Revolution and before myself: it was not I who betrayed him but he who betrayed his country. And we put him to death for it. It was only just. I have no regrets. He deserved to die. And yet I loved him. If you want to know the truth – I still love him. I write this on my death-bed. My heart was torn out long ago. Goodbye, old friend. I'm scribbling this to you because there are none of my friends left of those days. I don't suppose I'll come through this winter. It's getting worse and worse. They try to comfort me and tell me I'll be on my feet again, but I feel the truth. And I'm not afraid of it. Greetings and fraternity, as we used to say in those unforgettable times. For all that, our Revolution won through! I know you loved me, too, but only for a minute, for a fleeting second. Thank you even for that. You wouldn't know me now – I'm so ugly.

Yours ever,
Zaremba, Klavdia.'

Soon I learned that she had died, and imagined – no, not imagined but actually saw a view of the Urals from an altitude of several kilometres – at least two or three. The Ural mountains wrapped in dark winter clouds impenetrable to the eye, and only in one place, like a spring bubbling amid the folds of the desert, smoke was billowing up from under them; and this smoke I at first took for clouds, but then I realized from its different shades that this was the smoke of the city of Magnitogorsk below, and then the plane banked steeply over it and began circling down to land. It grew dark all round. And later I was driving from the aerodrome into town in a car which seemed to be pushing its way with a great effort through the dense clouds of the forty-degree frost, among the plaster-like Urals snows lighted like a congealed mass of boiled sweets by the small bronze-pink circle of the rayless Epiphany sun. Ahead a kind of mountain towered half way up the sky. It consisted of vari-coloured – coal-black, intense white, rusty-brown, lemon and amethyst – columns of smoke that were slowly climbing like sheep out of the two hundred chimneys of the huge metallurgical complex which lay in the gloom at the foot of this smoke mountain – a conglomeration of frost-coated blast furnaces, open-hearth furnaces, overhead gas-pipes writhing like giant pythons, trestles and high-tension transmission lines. The car seemed to drive into a dark cavern of smoke but, as it advanced, the walls of the cavern fell away, rays of sunlight pierced the topaz slabs of steam and smoke, a bright January day shone all around, and parks and avenues encrusted with thick layers of hoarfrost stood out clearly against a backdrop of intense lapis lazuli sky, above the narrow scrolled railings cast out of Magnitogorsk pig-iron. Every tree and every bush – cork elm, lilac, poplar, lime – which I had seen when they were still only saplings was now a miracle of winter beauty : some of them resembled the marvellous work of the Russian lace-makers, others stood along the straw-coloured and pink apartment blocks like sculptures of white stone, others bore a striking resemblance to the fragile growth of limestone coral of a bluish underwater kingdom, and others were like branchy antlers sprinkled with tiny, dust-like splinters of Urals gems, and the city of Magnitogorsk, submerged in clouds of sunlit mist, looked wonderfully fine in its regally Russian ermine robes – the city of a dream come true – and was seeing off on its last journey to the sounds of a brass band a lorry with a red coffin, very bright, almost radiant, like a bar of heated metal, in which there lay with her arms stretched out and her dark calcareous fingers clenched, and her eyes forever closed, Klavdia Zaremba, the girl from the Soviet and Party Workers School.

At night all the windows of the oxygen plant gleamed magically, like cells of a honeycomb, with a brilliant green-blue light and clouds of steam billowed over the warm Magnitogorsk Sea, into which the ancient Cossack chapel of the former Magnitnaya Fortress, mentioned in Pushkin's *History of Pugachev*, had disappeared forever like the mysterious city of Kitezh.

. . . Ash-tray. Greetings and fraternity. Angel of Death. Overseas ostrich. Book of dreams. Girl from the Party School. Klavdia Zaremba. Pcholkin. Two poets. . . .

I looked around me with surprise and noticed the flowering chestnuts and a cemetery wall with an open gate.

'Would madame and monsieur like to see this Russian emigré cemetery? It contains a curious little church in the ancient Novgorod style, built from drawings by the late Alexander Benois, the Russian artist. And, if you wish, you may also see the grave of the Nobel Prize winner Bunin, whom I believe you once knew. Gaston, stop here, please. We want to get out for a few minutes.'

A big-nosed old man with a few traces of military bearing, wearing a pince-nez, and with the white button of a hearing-aid in his ear – evidently an ex-Russian – was standing at the cemetery gate selling very large French lillies-of-the-valley. I selected a bunch from his flat rush basket and suddenly I recognized him. It was Petka Solovyov, the very same, but forty-five years older. My face must have expressed confusion, even horror, because he gave me a smile of practised self-esteem, revealing faulty teeth, and said:

'No, don't faint. You're quite right. It is me.'

'But you were shot,' I mumbled. 'I read the list in the paper with my own eyes.'

'I also read that list with my own eyes. But nothing of the kind actually happened. On the way from prison to the garage I jumped out of the lorry and got away over the wall of the second Christian cemetery. They fired a couple of shots at me from a rifle or a revolver but missed. And to avoid any unpleasantness the Angel of Death made up the number with some hold-up man or other and left my name on the list.'

I was utterly shaken, but I recovered. After all, why not? Such things had happened in those days.

'And what are you doing here?' I asked, just for the sake of asking something.

'You can see for yourself. Who am I? Neither one thing nor the other. I don't go in for politics, so you needn't be afraid of me. I'm quite loyal. Sometimes I read your papers, listen in to the radio and envy you. I was a fool. That's the honest truth, before God it is. And it's a bitter one too, you know. My grandchildren are French,' he added and I thought he was going to cry. 'I've just frittered my life away.'

'Do you remember Klavdia Zaremba?' I asked. 'She died not long ago in Magnitogorsk.'

'Who did you say?'

'Zaremba, Klavdia.'

219

He looked at me in dull concentration, as though he were deaf and dumb.

'Who is she?'

'In those days she was a member of the Komsomol.'

'Oh, yes, that little dark Komsomol girl. . . . Yes, yes. . . . I do remember vaguely. . . . But it's so many years ago now!' he added apologetically. 'You can't remember everything—'

And he began to rearrange the bunches in his basket.

What else was there for us to talk about?

Bunin's grave turned out to be something very different from what Bunin himself had imagined in middle life, while he was still in Russia:

'A tombstone, a metal plate, amid thick grass deep-rooted in the earth. . . . Beneath this same stone I'll quietly lie with others of my birth.'

And not like the one he had imagined in exile:

'Burn, blaze with all your hundred-coloured power, undying star, above my distant God-forgotten grave.'

The cemetery keeper, a carelessly dressed Russian gentleman with a rather ironical expression on his worn but still quite presentable face, which bore a fleeting resemblance to Petka Solovyov's, led us down a straight path, past Orthodox crosses and lofty tombs, and stopped beside a grey granite cross of somewhat unusual shape, a kind of military cross carved in stone, perhaps even a St George Cross, but rather squat, dark and heavy.

'Here is your Bunin. Have a good look,' the keeper said. 'As for the cross, the experts claim it's a copy of an old Russian or Byzantian monument, found in Pskov or somewhere, during some excavations or other – I can't tell you exactly which, because I know nothing whatever about archaeology. As for the grave, you see, it's not too much in the background and in quite good company.' And with a hospitable sweep of his arm he indicated the neighbouring graves, on which were inscribed some once illustrious Russian names now long since forgotten in Russia.

'They bring them here from all over the world – from Britain, Switzerland, even from America, by boat. Can't be helped. It's the most respectable Orthodox emigré cemetery to be had anywhere. Soon there won't be a single vacant plot left. We have already started putting two in one grave – as long as they are of the same family, of course. For instance, not long ago we buried Vera Nikolayevna in the same grave as Ivan Alexeyevich Bunin – at his feet. So now, at last, they're together again, both lying under the same cross.'

With a proprietary air he pushed aside with his foot a few broken crocks, withered flowers, funeral ribbons that had not yet faded and the wire frame of a small, typically French ring-shaped wreath. . . .

'The remains of her funeral,' he remarked fastidiously. 'They still haven't cleared away the rubbish. I shall have to give that watchman a good talking-to. Oho !' he said, looking up anxiously at the sky, where above the blue fir-trees and the candle-sticks of the flowering chestnuts, from behind which peeped the blue dome and white walls of a delightful ancient Russian church, there had gathered unnoticed some darkish stormclouds heavily diluted with white, and all of a sudden a streak of light shot up like a flame along a powder fuse, flashed right overhead with a dry snap like a Christmas cracker, and faint rumbles of April thunder came tumbling down, like a small mountain landslide.

. . . Ten o'clock, Moscow Time. We are broadcasting a programme of light music. . . .

Was this really the end?

The light-blue downpour hovered over the cemetery roses, over the yellow-red fingers of the bignonias, over the stone cross with the gold-inscribed names of Bunin and of Vera Nikolayevna lying faithfully at his feet, a sweet, dear old Russian woman – a Moscow girl student – on whose grave I placed the bunch of lilies-of-the-valley, but in so doing could not help remembering Ivan Alexeyevich's lines:

'Cold airs still drifted through the naked groves. . . .
Among the withered leaves you gleamed – and your damp
fragrance, moistly fresh yet stringent, with my young soul
became forever kin.'

'But where is Ivan Alexeyevich's favourite ash-tray?' I
asked during my last visit to Vera Nikolayevna. 'You remember, the one that always used to stand on the round
polished table at the Bukovetskys' house in Knyazheskaya
Street? Has it survived?'

'Do you remember it?' Vera Nikolayevna asked, and her
aged, bloodlessly pale face became animated for a second.

'I shall never forget it,' I replied.

She stood for a moment looking straight into my eyes
with profound and gentle sorrow, then went into another
room and returned carrying in her big rheumaticky hands
the ash-tray that was so agonizingly familiar and dear to me.

'This one?' she asked.

I made no reply, for I was unable to tear my glance from
that thin brass bowl with its Eastern ornament, which now
seemed to me much smaller than it used to be, as though it
had shrunk with age. It had not been polished for a long time
and it no longer burned with a feverish glow, and inside it
had turned quite black, like the censer that Bunin had once
found in hills of Sicily. . . .

Bignonia. Ode to the Revolution. Four times blessed.

'And you, my heart, with fire and fragrance filled, forget
it not. Burn, too, until to blackness charred.'

Or better still:

'Then play, fit to burst the aorta, with a cat's head in your
mouth. Three devils there were and you're the fourth – the
last, lovely devil in full flower!'

Peredelkino
1964-1967